**STECK-VAUGHN**
GED

EXERCISE BOOK

SOCIAL STUDIES

Virginia A. Lowe

Steck-Vaughn Adult Education Advisory Council

Donna D. Amstutz
Asst. Project Director
Northern Area Adult Education Service Center
Northern Illinois University
DeKalb, Illinois

Sharon K. Darling
President, National Center for Family Literacy
Louisville, Kentucky

Roberta Pittman
Director, Project C3 Adult Basic Education
Detroit Public Schools
Detroit, Michigan

Elaine Shelton
President, Shelton Associates
Consultant, Competency-Based Adult Education
Austin, Texas

STECK-VAUGHN
C O M P A N Y
A Subsidiary of National Education Corporation

About the Author

Virginia A. Lowe is an author, teacher, editor, and test-writer in the field of adult education. Virginia holds an M.A. in English from the University of Oregon and is pursuing doctoral work in folklore at Indiana University. Virginia has experience writing test items for the GED Testing Service and has edited GED preparatory books. She has also been an ABE/GED instructor in Indiana. Virginia also has published articles on historical aspects of folklore.

Acknowledgments

Grateful acknowledgment is made to the following authors, agents, and publishers for permission to reprint copyrighted materials.

American Psychological Association; for information used in the diagram of "The Interpersonal Behavior Cycle." Copyright 1963 by the American Psychological Association. Adapted and reprinted by permission. **(p. 50)**

Associated Press; for information used in pie graph from "Poll Says Americans Approve of Bush's Performance." Copyright 1989 by the Associated Press. **(p. 44)** From "Schools Merely Average" by Jill Lawrence. Copyright 1989 by the Associated Press. **(p. 45)**

Business Insurance; bar graph of Comprehensive Health Plan Costs from *Business Insurance*, January 9, 1989, p. 1. Copyright © 1989 by Crain Communications, Inc. All rights reserved. **(p. 30)**

Dow Jones & Company, Inc.; logo for "Wall Street's Recession" courtesy of *The Wall Street Journal*. Copyright © 1989 Dow Jones & Company, Inc. **(p. 32)**

Harcourt Brace Jovanovich; from *The American Presidency* by Clinton Rossiter. Copyright © 1956 by Clinton Rossiter and renewed 1984 by Mary Crane Rossiter, Caleb Rossiter, David Rossiter, and Winton Rossiter, reprinted by permission of Harcourt Brace Jovanovich, Inc. **(p. 41)**

William Hoest and *Parade* magazine; cartoon on lawyers by William Hoest. Copyright © 1989. Reprinted courtesy of Hoest and *Parade* magazine. **(p. 50)**

Holt, Rinehart and Winston, Inc.; adapted Figure 2 from *Ulithi: A Micronesian Design for Living* by William A. Lessa. Copyright © 1966 by Holt, Rinehart and Winston, Inc., reprinted by permission of the publisher. **(p. 68)**

Houghton Mifflin Company; excerpt from *The Affluent Society* by John Kenneth Galbraith. Copyright 1958, 1969, 1976, 1984 by John Kenneth Galbraith. Reprinted by permission of Houghton Mifflin Company. **(p. 31)**

Joint Council on Economic Education; from *A Framework for Teaching the Basic Concepts* by Phillip Saunders, G.L. Bach, James D. Calderwood, and W.L. Hansen. Copyright © 1977, 1984 by the Joint Council on Economic Education. **(p. 27)**

Life magazine and Rockwell Associates, Inc.; "Sightseeing in 1920" from *Life* magazine, 1902. Used with permission. **(p. 21)**

Dr. Maurice Lorr and Dr. Douglas McNair; information used in the diagram "The Interpersonal Behavior Cycle". Copyright 1965 by Dr. Maurice Lorr and Dr. Douglas McNair. Adapted and reprinted by permission. **(p. 50)**

Continued on page 107

Staff Credits

Supervising Editor: Carolyn M. Hall
Designer: John J. Harrison

1992 EDITION ISBN 0-8114-4480-5

CONTENTS

INTRODUCTION

The *Steck-Vaughn Exercise Book: Social Studies* provides you with practice in answering the types of questions found on the actual GED Social Studies Test. It can be used with the *Steck-Vaughn GED Social Studies* book or with the *Steck-Vaughn Complete GED Preparation* book. Cross references to pages in the other two books are supplied for your convenience on exercise pages 4–47. This exercise book has two sections: practice exercises and simulated tests.

PRACTICE EXERCISE SECTION

The GED Social Studies Test examines your ability to understand, apply, analyze, and evaluate information in five social studies areas. The practice exercise section is divided into the same five content areas by chapter. The geography chapter examines topography and location of major features of the landscape in the United States and globally. The history chapter examines American history from the founding of the United States to the Vietnam War. The economics chapter covers the study of the production, distribution, and consumption of goods and services. The political science chapter covers governmental institutions and processes and the relationships between political and economic processes. The last chapter, behavioral science, examines human actions and generalizations about human behavior in society.

SIMULATED TESTS SECTION

The second main part of this workbook consists of two complete full-length Simulated GED Social Studies Tests. Each Simulated Test has the same number of items as the GED Test. In addition, each test provides practice with similar item types that are found on the GED Test. The Simulated Tests can help you decide if you are ready to take the GED Social Studies Test. To benefit most from the Simulated Tests Section, take each test under the same time restrictions as you will have for the actual GED Test. For each test, complete the 64 items within 85 minutes. Space the two examinations apart by at least a week.

CONTENT AREAS

The GED Social Studies Test is divided into five content areas: **geography, history, economics, political science,** and **behavioral science.**

The short reading passages on the GED Test usually have only one question following them. Longer reading passages have several related questions. Approximately 15% of the passages and related items are about geography, 25% are about history, 20% are about economics, 20% are about political science, and 20% are about behavioral science. From your life experience, you may easily relate to these items.

COGNITIVE LEVELS

All of the questions on the GED Social Studies Test are multiple-choice. You will not be tested on your knowledge of social studies, but rather on your ability to understand, apply, and analyze social studies concepts. Following is an explanation of the four cognitive levels of questions that you will practice in this book and that are found on the GED Test.

1. **Comprehension** items require you to identify restated information or information that is paraphrased. They require you to summarize ideas or identify implications.

2. **Application** items require you to apply a rule and make a prediction of what would happen in a similar instance. They require you to use the information provided to solve a problem.

3. **Analysis** items require you to classify information. Sometimes you will be asked to distinguish or compare and contrast information presented.

4. **Evaluation** items test your ability to identify opinions and/or recognize assumptions. Other evaluation items ask you to identify cause and effect relationships.

Approximately 20% of the items are comprehension, 30% are application, 30% are analysis, and 20% are evaluation.

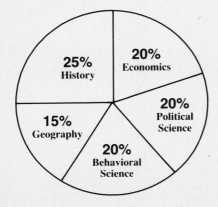

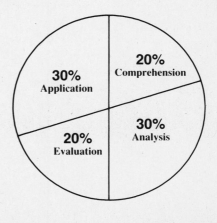

Graphic Illustrations

Approximately one-third of the items relate to a drawing, chart, map, or graph. Practice with graphic illustrations is essential to develop the skills to interpret information presented on the GED Social Studies Test. Always read the title, key, and any other information associated with the illustration before answering any questions.

Answers

The answer sections give complete explanations of why an answer is correct, and why the other answer choices are incorrect. Sometimes by studying the reason an answer is incorrect, you can learn to avoid a similar problem in the future.

Analysis of Performance Charts

After each Simulated Test, an Analysis of Performance Chart will help you determine if you are ready to take the GED Social Studies Test. The charts give a breakdown by content area (geography, history, economics, political science, and behavioral science) and by question type (comprehension, application, analysis, and evaluation). By completing these charts, you can determine your own strengths and weaknesses as they relate to the social studies area.

Correlation Chart

The following correlation chart shows how the sections of this exercise book relate to sections of other Steck-Vaughn GED preparation books. You can refer to these two books for further instruction or review.

CONTENT AREAS	Geography	History	Economics	Political Science	Behavioral Science
BOOK TITLES Steck-Vaughn GED Exercise Book	p. 4-14	p. 15-25	p. 26-35	p. 36-46	p. 47-54
Steck-Vaughn GED Social Studies	p. 26-63	p. 64-127	p. 128-167	p. 168-217	p. 218-247
Steck-Vaughn Complete GED Preparation	p. 277-289	p. 256-276	p. 290-302	p. 303-319	p. 320-336

UNIT 1 PRACTICE EXERCISES

Chapter 1 Geography ❏

Directions: Choose the one best answer for each item below.

Items 1–4 refer to the following passage.

For several weeks early every spring, thousands of sandhill cranes land on the banks of the Platte River near Kearney, Nebraska. Here they feed and rest for their long northward migration. But this section of the Platte, once almost a mile wide, has been reduced to only several hundred feet by upstream dams which regulate the early spring floods. The cranes' natural rest stop may be further threatened by the building of a new dam that would divert water from the Platte for the use of Denver and possibly other cities. This project has resulted in a dispute between the water planners and environmentalists.

1. Which of the following statements is suggested by the passage?

   (1) The sandhill crane population is in danger of extinction.
   (2) Nebraska no longer receives enough rainfall.
   (3) Flooding is still a problem for Denver and other cities.
   (4) Denver does not have an adequate water supply.
   (5) The Platte River is more than sufficient for the needs of both humans and birds.

2. If other areas follow the example of diverting water from already depleted rivers, the result will most likely be

   (1) the further growth of cities in water-poor areas
   (2) a mass relocation of animal sanctuaries
   (3) a serious environmental problem
   (4) a revitalization of river systems
   (5) a whole new network of rivers

3. Which of the following statements is most likely to be an argument presented in favor of the dam project?

   (1) Human use of resources is more important than preservation of a single bird's habitat.
   (2) The birds can easily find somewhere else to rest.
   (3) About half the water will be needed for watering lawns.
   (4) Annual flooding will still take place on the Platte River.
   (5) The cranes will be allowed to use the dam's reservoir as a watering hole.

4. Environmentalists involved in this dispute most likely will

   (1) eventually agree with the water planners
   (2) try to stop construction of the dam
   (3) urge a diversion of water away from Denver
   (4) use the Platte River problem as an example of cruelty to animals
   (5) try to restrict further spring flooding of the Platte

See Also ▶ | Social Studies Complete Preparation | pages 26–63 pages 277–289

Sun City, Arizona

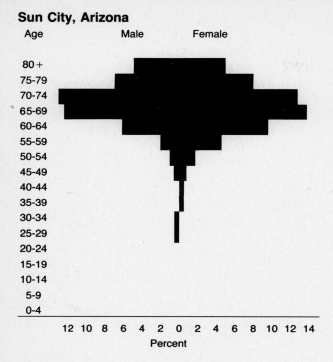

5. According to the graph, which of the following is most likely true of Sun City?

   (1) The population is rapidly declining.
   (2) The climate attracts people of retirement age.
   (3) The population growth rate is fairly steady.
   (4) Sun City is a popular family vacation spot.
   (5) There are twice as many women as men.

6. According to the information on the graph, which of the following public facilities would you expect to find the most of in Sun City?

   (1) high schools
   (2) colleges
   (3) hospitals
   (4) day care centers
   (5) libraries

7. Hurricanes are large rotating tropical storms with winds up to 150 miles per hour and torrential rains that can produce almost instant flooding. People living in hurricane-prone areas would be most likely to prefer which of the following architectural features?

   (1) dirt floor cellars
   (2) high-rise apartment buildings
   (3) glass-enclosed patios
   (4) ranch style buildings
   (5) New England style gable roofs

8. In 1957, France, Belgium, Luxembourg, West Germany, Italy, and the Netherlands formed the European Economic Community, also known as the Common Market. This move improved their economies by removing the tariffs (taxes) on mutually imported or exported goods. Even when countries such as Denmark and Great Britain joined the group, the Common Market continued to make sense because

   (1) all Western European nations are in financial trouble
   (2) shipping distances between the nations are quite small
   (3) world peace depends on the cooperation of dissimilar cultures
   (4) each nation grows completely different crops
   (5) all these nations have adjoining borders

Items 9–10 refer to the following map.

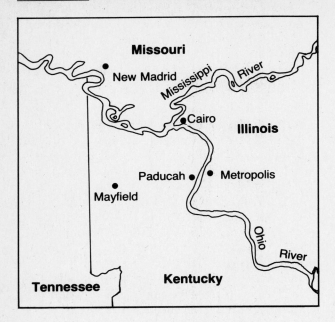

9. According to the map, which of the following statements is not true?

  (1) The Mississippi River forms a natural boundary between Illinois and Missouri.
  (2) The Ohio River forms a natural boundary between Kentucky and Illinois.
  (3) Three states meet at the junction of two rivers.
  (4) The natural boundary between Missouri and Kentucky is the Ohio River.
  (5) It is possible to travel down the Ohio to the Mississippi.

10. At which of the following cities would a shipping company be most likely to set up a main office?

  (1) Paducah
  (2) Metropolis
  (3) Mayfield
  (4) Cairo
  (5) New Madrid

Items 11–12 refer to the following passage.

    Latitude and longitude are imaginary lines that form a grid pattern around the earth. Latitudes, or parallels, run east and west at equal distances from each other, never meeting. Latitudes are measured in degrees (°) northward from the Equator (0°) to the North Pole (90° N) and southward to the South Pole (90° S). Longitudes, or meridians, run north and south meeting at the poles. These lines are measured eastward for 180° from the Prime Meridian in Greenwich, England and westward for 180°.

11. From the passage it can be asssumed that Greenwich, England is at

  (1) 0° latitude
  (2) 180° E longitude
  (3) 90° W longitude
  (4) 0° longitude
  (5) the Equator

12. For which of the following would knowledge of longitude and latitude be most important?

  (1) river transportation
  (2) city driving
  (3) ocean navigation
  (4) rural driving
  (5) cross-country hiking

Items 13–16 refer to the following maps.

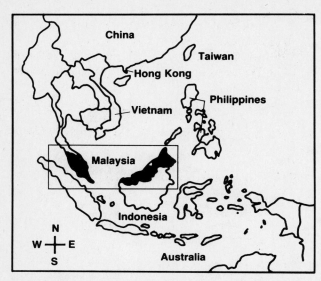

Inset Map

13. Which of the following is not a city in Malaysia?

    (1) Kuala Lumpur
    (2) Ipoh
    (3) Brunei
    (4) Kuching
    (5) Kota Kinabalu

14. People living in East Malaysia probably find trade easiest with

    (1) Thailand
    (2) Australia
    (3) China
    (4) Indonesia
    (5) Vietnam

15. Which of the following statements best explains why Singapore, which had united in 1963 with Sabah and Sarawak to join Malaysia, is now an independent nation?

    (1) Singapore was granted independence from British rule in 1957.
    (2) Singapore was dominated by a Chinese, rather than Malay, government.
    (3) The island was too far from the Malay peninsula.
    (4) The islanders felt isolated.
    (5) Officials in Singapore believed that Sabah and Sarawak were too close to the island.

16. Considering that Malaysia's religious groups include Muslims and Hindus, which of the following foods is most likely the main source of protein in Malaysia?

    (1) rice
    (2) beef
    (3) pork
    (4) fruit
    (5) fish

Items 17–20 refer to the following diagram.

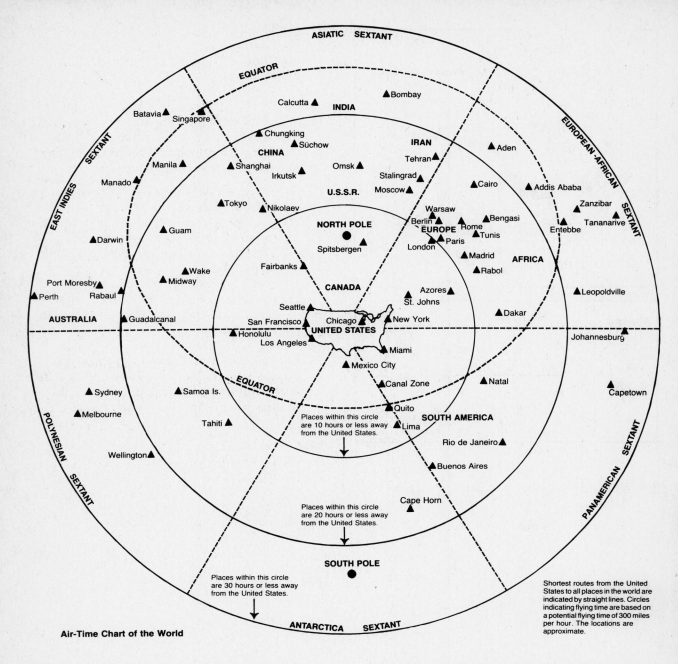

Air-Time Chart of the World

17. The information on the diagram suggests that

   (1) air travel has changed people's perspective on world geography
   (2) most people flew out of Chicago in 1943
   (3) the Poles are closer than we thought they were
   (4) the Equator does not really run around the center of the globe
   (5) air traffic runs only in straight lines

18. In which of the following ways would a similar diagram drawn in the 1990's differ from the one above?

   (1) The shortest route line would be changed.
   (2) Tehran would be removed from the diagram.
   (3) The flying time estimates would be shorter.
   (4) The location of Tokyo would be changed.
   (5) The United States would not be in the middle of the diagram.

8

19. Why would the information on the diagram influence a development of more overseas United States military bases?

   (1) It indicates that Americans have easy access to foreign countries.
   (2) It suggests that enemy planes could reach the U.S. quickly.
   (3) It reveals that Europe is too close for comfort.
   (4) It shows how unprotected Australia is.
   (5) It reveals how few overseas bases there are.

20. If the diagram indicates that this is a small world after all, what would be the best conclusion for major world powers to reach?

   (1) The military can start using smaller planes.
   (2) World peace should be their next objective.
   (3) Hand-to-hand fighting will be back in style.
   (4) Nuclear war is inevitable.
   (5) Space is the new frontier.

21. Demography is the study of population distribution. Density of population is measured by the number of people living in a square mile of land. Cities of more than one million inhabitants are called population nuclei. Which of the following is not an example of demography?

   (1) In 1966, New Zealand had a density of 23 per square mile.
   (2) In 1980, there were as many people over the age of 30 in the United States as there were under 30.
   (3) Between 1940 and 1950, the population of South Dakota rose by only 1.5%.
   (4) Indiana has a land area of 35,936 square miles.
   (5) New York City, with over 7,071,000 inhabitants, is one of the larger metropolitan nuclei in the United States.

22. Scientists have found new evidence that the earth is warming up due to the greenhouse effect. Since 1982, the temperature of the world's oceans has risen 0.2 degrees Fahrenheit each year. If the gases that result from the use of fossil fuels are partially responsible for this problem, then our best course of action is to

   (1) start using oil instead of coal and gas
   (2) find alternate sources of energy
   (3) find a way to cool the oceans
   (4) find a way to contain the gases
   (5) prepare for warmer winters

Items 23–24 refer to the following map.

North America in 1783

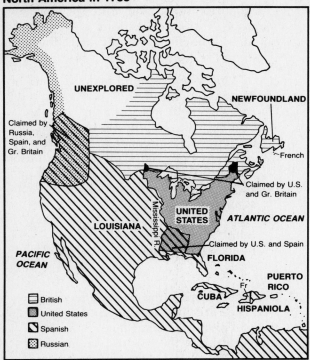

UNEXPLORED

NEWFOUNDLAND

French

Claimed by Russia, Spain, and Gr. Britain

Claimed by U.S. and Gr. Britain

Mississippi R.

UNITED STATES

ATLANTIC OCEAN

LOUISIANA

PACIFIC OCEAN

Claimed by U.S. and Spain

FLORIDA

PUERTO RICO

Fr

CUBA

HISPANIOLA

☐ British
▨ United States
◩ Spanish
▨ Russian

23. Which of the following best explains why Russia claimed land on the Northwest coast?

   (1) The Louisiana Territory was already claimed by Spain.
   (2) Russia didn't want to interfere with Spain.
   (3) Russian ships had fairly easy access to the Alaskan Territory by sea.
   (4) The Russian government wanted to claim land far from the United States.
   (5) The Northwest coast was the only land left unclaimed.

24. Which of the following is best explained by the information on this map?

   (1) the location of the Mexico-United States border
   (2) the purchase of the Louisiana Territory from France by the United States
   (3) the cold war between the United States and the Soviet Union
   (4) the prevalence of Spanish place names in California
   (5) the definition of the Canada-United States border

Items 25–26 refer to the following map.

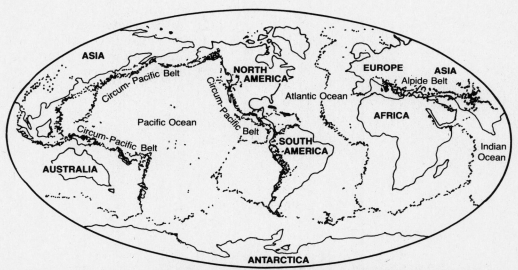

ASIA

Circum-Pacific Belt

NORTH AMERICA

EUROPE

ASIA
Alpide Belt

Atlantic Ocean

Pacific Ocean

Circum-Pacific Belt

AFRICA

Circum-Pacific Belt

SOUTH AMERICA

Indian Ocean

AUSTRALIA

ANTARCTICA

Almost all the world's major earthquakes occur in the circum-Pacific belt and the Alpide belt.

25. According to the map, earthquakes are most frequently associated with

   (1) rivers
   (2) lakes
   (3) oceans
   (4) mountains
   (5) valleys

26. Which of the following major world cities would most likely be affected by earthquakes?

   (1) New York, New York
   (2) Chicago, Illinois
   (3) Sidney, Australia
   (4) Johannesburg, South Africa
   (5) Acapulco, Mexico

The state of Oregon has over 97,000 square miles of land. It is surrounded by the states of Washington, Idaho, Nevada, California, and the Pacific Ocean. The western third of Oregon is dramatically divided from the rest of the state by the Cascade Mountain Range. To the west of the Cascades, the land is drenched in rain for most of the year and is lush with vegetation. To the east of the Cascades, dust storms parch the land to the extent that many of the lakes listed on maps are referred to as dry. Much of Oregon is forested, even to the east where the woodlands are scattered and less dense. But due to the ever-increasing need for lumber, even the forests in the mountains and to the west are being cut too quickly for new growth to replace the old.

27. Which of the following statements best explains why the Bureau of Land Management might support the recycling of paper?

(1) The steady rainfalls in western Oregon occur through most of the year.
(2) Large-scale forest fires are frequent.
(3) Tree planting teams have been working on reforestation for at least twenty years.
(4) Oregon was one of the first states to pass a bottle recycling bill.
(5) There are not enough lumber mills in Oregon.

28. Which of the following slogans is supported by data in the passage?

(1) Only You Can Prevent Forest Fires
(2) It's More Than a Tree; It's a Home
(3) Oregonians Don't Tan; They Rust
(4) Go West, Young Man
(5) Keep Our Cities Clean

29. Eastern Oregon is drier than the western section because

(1) there is more land to the east
(2) many of the lakes have long since dried up
(3) frequent storms carry moisture into Washington
(4) the Cascades block the wet ocean winds
(5) the scattered forests don't retain much moisture

30. Crops grown in eastern Oregon are most likely similar to those grown in

(1) California
(2) Washington
(3) Ohio
(4) Iowa
(5) Idaho

Items 31–34 refer to the following chart.

Geographic Distribution of U.S. Population, 1930–1970 (in percentages)

YEAR	CENTRAL CITIES	SUBURBS	RURAL AREAS & SMALL TOWNS
1930	31.8	18.0	50.2
1940	31.6	19.5	48.9
1950	32.3	23.8	43.9
1960	32.6	30.7	36.7
1970	31.4	37.6	31.0

Source: Adapted from U.S. Bureau of the Census, *Decennial Censuses*, 1930–1970 (Washington, U.S. Government Printing Office).

31. According to the chart, during a forty-year period, the percentage of the United States population living in cities

    (1) dropped dramatically
    (2) increased dramatically
    (3) rose steadily
    (4) remained fairly stable
    (5) rose and fell dramatically

32. If many city dwellers were moving to the suburbs during the 1960's and 1970's, which of the following best explains the percentages for central cities during those years?

    (1) a major increase in the national birthrate
    (2) growing unemployment in small towns and rural areas
    (3) the building of high-rise apartments
    (4) the growth of a thriving middle class
    (5) increased highway construction in rural areas

33. Which of the following groups was most likely affected the least by the population shifts between 1950 and 1970?

    (1) city government officials
    (2) automobile manufacturers
    (3) highway construction workers
    (4) housing contractors
    (5) gas station operators

34. If the trend indicated in this chart continues, the population distribution in the year 2000 most likely will be

    (1) 32.9% living in rural areas and small towns
    (2) 56.3% living in the suburbs
    (3) 16.5% living in the suburbs
    (4) 56.3% living in rural areas and small towns
    (5) 37.6% living in the suburbs

35. When a massive oil spill occurred in Prince William Sound, Alaska on March 23, 1989, a large oil skimmer sailed from the Soviet Union to assist in the cleanup of the Alaskan coast. Which of the following statements is best supported by this information?

    (1) Major world powers are realizing the importance of mutual cooperation in preserving the ecology.
    (2) Oil spills have become a routine problem for the Soviet Union.
    (3) The United States is no longer capable of handling its own environmental problems.
    (4) The Soviet Union was aware that this was the largest oil spill ever to have occurred.
    (5) The political differences between the United States and the Soviet Union have been settled.

36. The trade imbalance between the United States and Japan has narrowed since 1984 when Japan imported less than $30 billion of merchandise from the United States. In 1988, of Japan's total imports, $40 billion came from the United States. What additional information is needed to determine the amount of the trade imbalance in 1988?

    (1) the total amount of Japan's imports in 1984
    (2) the total amount of Japan's imports in 1988
    (3) the amount the United States imported in 1984
    (4) the amount the United States imported in 1988
    (5) the total amount of United States exports in 1988

37. You are traveling from Indianapolis, Indiana to Sioux Falls, South Dakota. Your map shows the location of major cities, roads, and rivers. It shows direction and changes in elevation. It even indicates rest areas and campgrounds. Which of the following will you be unable to determine using your map?

(1) if Chicago lies along your route
(2) if you can stop for a picnic along the way
(3) whether Sioux Falls is east or west of Rapid City
(4) how many rivers you will be crossing
(5) how far you will have to travel

38. Panama, a long, narrow country, links the North and South American continents. The Panama Canal crosses the width of Panama from one ocean to the other. Interestingly, the Pacific Ocean end of the canal lies east of the Atlantic Ocean end. What does this reveal about Panama's geographic position?

(1) The Pacific Ocean is east of Panama.
(2) The Atlantic Ocean is south of Panama.
(3) Panama's length extends from north to south.
(4) Panama's length extends from east to west.
(5) Panama lies across the Equator.

Items 39–42 refer to the following maps.

Sources of Immigration, 1871–1910

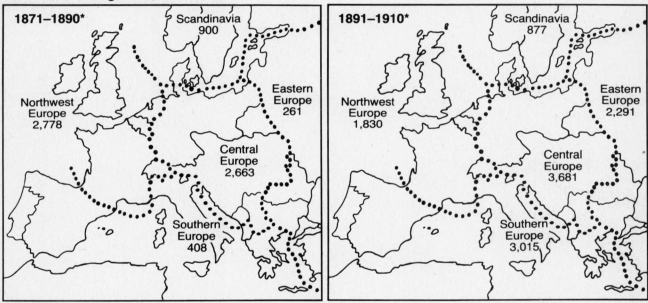

*Immigration in thousands

39. Which statement best explains why the ethnic make-up of many American cities changed considerably over a forty-year period?

(1) Thousands of people from different cultural groups arrived in America from 1871 to 1910.
(2) Immigration from Northwest Europe was highest between 1871 and 1891.
(3) Limits on immigration quotas were established in 1914.
(4) America really was the new land of milk and honey.
(5) Immigrants from the Orient were arriving to work on the new cross-country railroad.

40. In 1910, New York City had half as many Italians as the city of Naples. This is best explained by

(1) the decline of Naples as a major city
(2) the fact that over 3,453,000 people had immigrated from Southern Europe
(3) the fact that 6,344,000 people had immigrated from Central Europe
(4) the map's evidence that 3,453 of the immigrants were Italian
(5) the large Italian population of New York City today

41. Which of the following American monuments best represents the hopes of the immigrants?

(1) the Lincoln Memorial
(2) the Liberty Bell
(3) the Statue of Liberty
(4) the Washington Monument
(5) Mount Rushmore

42. The pattern of immigration from 1891 to 1910 supports the conclusion that

(1) Scandinavians were no longer interested in immigration
(2) shortly after the turn of the century, language barriers forced many new arrivals into low-paying factory jobs
(3) by 1910 the immigrants had begun to adjust to their new surroundings
(4) only Eastern Europeans were interested in finding a new way of life
(5) more and more European intellectuals were becoming aware of the opportunities that America offered

Answers begin on page 94.

Directions: Choose the one best answer for each item below.

Items 1–4 refer to the following passage.

Christopher Columbus sailed the ocean in 1492 in search of a westward route to the Far East. He not only discovered the New World, but he also started a trend in the Old World that eventually led to the colonization of the Americas. After Columbus claimed the West Indies for Spain, John Cabot claimed Newfoundland in 1497 for England. Yet a third Italian, Amerigo Vespucci, was sent by Spain in 1499 to sail along part of the South American coast. He was followed during the next forty years by Vasco Núñez de Balboa who found the Isthmus of Panama, Juan Ponce de León who reached Florida, Hernando Cortés who penetrated Mexico, Hernando de Soto who discovered the Mississippi River, and Francisco Vasquez de Coronado who explored what is now the southwestern part of the United States. In 1524, France sent Italian John Verrazano along the coast of North America. In 1534, Jacques Cartier claimed the Saint Lawrence River Region for France. And in 1609, Henry Hudson discovered the Hudson River and the land which is now New York City for the Dutch.

1. Details of the passage best support the conclusion that

   (1) all the explorers found what they were looking for
   (2) European sailors were in search of adventure
   (3) Italians were skilled navigators
   (4) trade routes to the Far East were finally discovered
   (5) the world is round

2. In the early days of exploration of the New World, most of the land was

   (1) uninhabited
   (2) open to new settlers
   (3) claimed by Spain
   (4) claimed by Christopher Columbus
   (5) disputed by the various explorers

3. The routes of the early explorers best explain

   (1) the later colonization patterns
   (2) why so many Europeans went to sea
   (3) how New York and Miami got their names
   (4) why the official language in the United States is English
   (5) why the Panama Canal was built

4. Which of the following best explains why the newly discovered lands were not named after either Columbus or Cabot?

   (1) Neither was well-known enough.
   (2) Neither had really reached the mainland.
   (3) Spain claimed the right to name the new lands.
   (4) Both sailors were more interested in wealth than in fame.
   (5) Vespucci brought home the first evidence of the New World's wealth.

The thirteen original English colonies were established by corporations, like today's joint stock companies, or by proprietary agencies of one or more people. All received grants of territory from the English Crown. The members of these groups were motivated by interests in profiting from trade, extending English power, converting the native Americans to Christianity, and pursuing religious freedom for oppressed sects. Many were also motivated to provide a new start for the poor and destitute, thus easing the burden on English workhouses and debtors' prisons.

5. Which of the following was not a reason for colonization?

   (1) attaining religious freedom
   (2) gaining political independence
   (3) expanding political domination
   (4) doing charitable work
   (5) making money

6. According to the passage, why might some English citizens have become indentured servants to established colonials, thus giving up their freedom for up to seven years in exchange for passage and land of their own after their indenture was over?

   (1) Many of these people were running from the law.
   (2) They could not otherwise afford to make a new life in the Americas.
   (3) Their religious principles required them to humble themselves.
   (4) They were used to being servants in England.
   (5) They were misled by false promises from the corporations.

7. It can be inferred from the passage that widespread and systematic colonization was made possible

   (1) because life in England was intolerable
   (2) by grants of land subject to the English Crown
   (3) because of improved ocean navigation
   (4) by the abundance of natural resources in the Americas
   (5) because people recognized the importance of religious tolerance

John Locke, an English philosopher of the seventeenth century, wrote the following excerpts:

"There is therefore...another way whereby governments are dissolved, and that is when the legislative or the prince, either of them, act contrary to their trust. First, the legislative acts against the trust reposed in them when they endeavor to invade the property of the subject, and to make themselves or any part of the community masters or arbitrary disposers of the lives, liberties, or fortunes of the people.

"For the people having reserved to themselves the choice of their representatives as the fence to their properties, could do it for no other end but that they might always be freely chosen, freely act and advise as the necessity of the commonwealth and the public good should upon examination and mature debate be judged to require."

8. According to the passage, Locke believed that

   (1) legislators can dissolve governments
   (2) people have the right to privacy of property
   (3) governments do not have an obligation to their people
   (4) people should have no say in who represents them
   (5) government representatives are responsible for property line fences

9. Locke most likely would have supported

   (1) colonists who objected to having to house British troops
   (2) the British government violating a treaty with the Ottawa Indians
   (3) a group of angry colonists who raided a band of Indian Christian converts
   (4) Prime Minister Grenville who decided to tax American colonists to help repay debts from the Seven Years War
   (5) France when it ceded its North American holdings to Britain

10. Which of the following expressions best represents the American colonists' adoption of Locke's principles?

    (1) Give me liberty or give me death.
    (2) No taxation without representation.
    (3) I have not yet begun to fight.
    (4) The British are coming!
    (5) Join or die.

11. John Locke would have disagreed with the view that King George III deserved the American Revolution because he was feeble-minded on the grounds that

    (1) the argument attacks the person rather than the issue of a violation of rights
    (2) a king can govern well even if he is mentally ill
    (3) the statement is not proof that King George was feeble-minded
    (4) no king deserves rebellion of his subjects
    (5) King George deserved sympathy

Items 12–13 refer to the following graph.

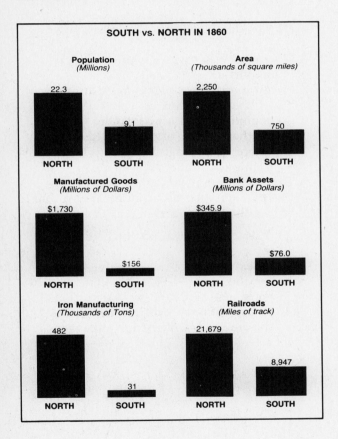

12. Before the Civil War, according to the graph, the North

    (1) had more slaves than the South
    (2) covered less territory than the South
    (3) had a more experienced government
    (4) had greater resources and labor forces than the South
    (5) was more committed to winning the war than was the South

13. Judging from the graph, which of the following statements is most justified?

    (1) It was through sheer determination on the part of the South that the war lasted four years.
    (2) Confederate leaders had no business conducting a war.
    (3) The North won because of moral superiority.
    (4) Slavery was not of economic benefit to the South.
    (5) An agrarian economy has no chance against an industrial economy.

Items 14–17 refer to the following graph.

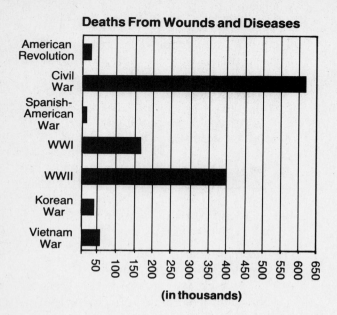

Deaths From Wounds and Diseases

American Revolution
Civil War
Spanish-American War
WWI
WWII
Korean War
Vietnam War

50 100 150 200 250 300 350 400 450 500 550 600 650

(in thousands)

14. Based on the figures in the graph, the Civil War may best be described as

(1) the war between the states
(2) a well-fought war
(3) a major American tragedy
(4) a waste of time and money
(5) a good example for North and South Vietnam

15. The losses on both sides in the Civil War were especially hard for the nation to bear because

(1) neither side had enough soldiers
(2) friends and relatives were often among the enemy dead
(3) the abolition of slavery would have happened anyway
(4) the nation was in need of better soldiers
(5) the national birthrate had decreased

16. What is wrong with the opinion that because the death toll of the Civil War is almost equal to that of all the other wars shown on the graph, the Civil War was the most important?

(1) The death toll for other wars isn't given.
(2) World War I was obviously the most important.
(3) An internal conflict is not as important as one with a foreign enemy.
(4) Significance of a war cannot be judged by the number of people killed.
(5) There is nothing wrong with this opinion.

17. One of the major effects of the loss of life during the Civil War was most likely

(1) a serious disorganization of the labor force
(2) a destruction of credit ratings in the South
(3) an increase in banking transactions
(4) a surge of industrial growth
(5) the emergence of the carpetbagger

Items 18–21 refer to the following passage.

One of the first effects of the Industrial Revolution in America was on the lifestyles of craftspeople and farmers. Finding themselves in competition with machinery which could produce the same products more quickly and for lower prices, many craftspeople gave up their traditional work and turned to full-time farming. Some in rural areas moved to the cities to work in factories where their skills could be used. Still others turned to occupations that were related to their former crafts. For example, some cabinetmakers, who had often doubled as undertakers because they made the coffins, became full-time undertakers. Still others became innkeepers because they had a ready supply of furniture and maintenance skills.

The production of factory goods also affected farmers who had relied on the barter system for obtaining the items they could not make or grow themselves. Because they were no longer able to trade easily for what they needed, many farmers changed to cash-crop farming. This change often involved a need for more land. While self-sufficient farmers needed only enough land to grow food for their families and for trading purposes, cash-crop farmers had to grow enough to sell. The more land one had, the more cash one had. Cash-crop farmers also needed hired hands to help work the land and to run the machinery in order to farm the larger acreage. Some farmers finally moved to the cities because they couldn't raise or sell enough crops to survive.

18. Which conclusion may be drawn from the passage?

   (1) Only a few craftspeople and farmers were affected by the Industrial Revolution.
   (2) The Industrial Revolution was a welcome change for self-sufficient farmers.
   (3) The Industrial Revolution probably changed a large number of lifestyles in America.
   (4) The occupation of undertaker became very popular after the Industrial Revolution.
   (5) City factories quickly became overcrowded.

19. According to the passage, some craftspeople and farmers moved to the cities because

   (1) they had grown tired of country life
   (2) food was more plentiful in the cities
   (3) living in the country was hard work
   (4) they were looking for jobs
   (5) factory goods were more available in the cities

20. According to the passage, which of the following was not a result of the Industrial Revolution?

   (1) A number of farms increased their acreage.
   (2) Factory goods were cheaper than goods made by traditional craftspeople.
   (3) Factory jobs were available in the cities.
   (4) Some people had to find different occupations.
   (5) All self-sufficient farmers had to become cash-crop farmers.

21. Which of the following twentieth-century inventions would have effects most similar to those of the Industrial Revolution?

   (1) the microwave oven
   (2) the cellular telephone
   (3) computer technology
   (4) cable television
   (5) the jet propulsion engine

Item 22 refers to the following graph.

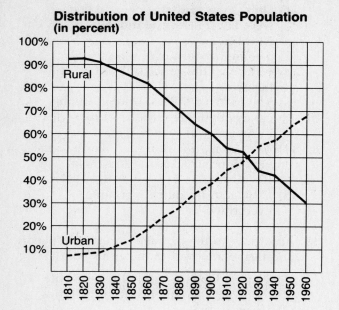

Distribution of United States Population (in percent)

22. Which of the following statements is best supported by the information in this graph?

(1) European immigrants were pouring into American cities before the turn of the century.
(2) Large-scale agribusinesses are responsible for driving people from their farms.
(3) Within one century, the American economy shifted from being primarily agrarian to a more industrial economy.
(4) People began leaving the cities after the turn of the century.
(5) The distribution of the United States population reached a balance in 1900.

Items 23–24 refer to the following passage.

As conditions changed in American cities during the late nineteenth century, city government was complicated by boards and committees and officials needed to handle new problems. The resulting confusion lead to the development of political machines that were made up of candidates and supporters who were more interested in having power than in the good of the people. These politicians often used bribery and graft to get into office.

23. These corrupt organizations may have been called machines because they

(1) were all very much alike
(2) manufactured votes
(3) were products of industrialization
(4) were very powerful
(5) helped to rebuild the cities

24. Illegal businesses such as gambling and prostitution benefited from political machines because

(1) the politicians ignored them
(2) the politicians were uninterested in law enforcement
(3) the businesses could pay corrupt politicians to leave them alone
(4) the politicians were the ones who ran those businesses
(5) the police were too busy investigating the politicians

Items 25–26 refer to the following cartoon.

SIGHTSEEING IN 1920.

The caption on this 1902 cartoon from *Life* reads as follows: "That depression down there is where New York City stood. But with all its skyscrapers and underground tunnels it suddenly sunk one day and they haven't been able to find it since."

25. According to the cartoon, the major cause for the disappearance of New York City is

(1) an earthquake
(2) the skyscrapers were too high
(3) the land could no longer support its weight
(4) too many people lived there
(5) it had become an underground city

26. The cartoonist is expressing the opinion that

(1) growth of a city is not always good
(2) people in 1920 will enjoy sightseeing
(3) American cities are health hazards
(4) the buildings in New York City are poorly constructed
(5) balloon flights are popular tourist attractions

Items 27–28 refer to the following cartoon.

THE PROGRESS OF ART.

27. Which of the following is the best alternative title for the cartoon?

(1) Too Much a Sign of the Times
(2) How To Get the Most Out of an Ad
(3) Strange Foods of the City
(4) The Most Effective Use of Art
(5) The Growth of American Business

28. The bag in the cartoon most likely represents

(1) improvements in advertising
(2) the increased cost of building in the city
(3) the money involved in advertising
(4) the results of eating brain food
(5) a rejection of old-fashioned art

Items 29–30 refer to the following passage.

Before World War II, women workers were not welcome in industrial jobs. But wartime labor shortages brought 2.5 million women to the factories. Many of these women, who were married and over thirty-five, became welders, toolmakers, and blast furnace operators.

29. The importance of the role these women played is best expressed

    (1) in the phrase "Rosie the riveter"
    (2) in the phrase "a woman's place is in the home"
    (3) in the phrase "a woman's work is never done"
    (4) in the phrase "keep the home fires burning"
    (5) by the actions of ax-wielding Carry Nation

30. Many women who remained in manufacturing in 1945 and were paid 65% of what men were paid for the same job were dissatisfied because

    (1) the women had gotten used to better wages
    (2) the men performed the jobs more efficiently
    (3) women had already proven that they could do the jobs
    (4) women no longer wanted to work in the home
    (5) they wanted to quit work and be housewives again

Items 31–32 refer to the following cartoon.

Reprinted by permission of UFS, Inc.

31. The boy wearing dark glasses in the cartoon is most likely

    (1) a potential high school dropout
    (2) a student interested in literature
    (3) a music student
    (4) a student with poor math skills
    (5) an excellent student

32. By including the notice on the bulletin board, the cartoonist is suggesting that in a highly technological society

    (1) American students will do very well
    (2) American students may not be as well prepared as students from other countries
    (3) American students rank very high in reading skills
    (4) math and science are no longer important
    (5) computers are eliminating the need to study math and science

Items 33-36 refer to the following passage.

The decade from 1960 to 1969 will be remembered by many as a period of social and political unrest in the United States. During this time, many people despaired over the clothing worn and the music listened to by American youth. However, that music was often a sign of the times and a reflection of the tensions and changes that were affecting much of American society. In the early sixties, questions about social justice were raised by songs such as Bob Dylan's "Blowin' in the Wind" and "The Chimes of Freedom Flashing" which echoed the civil rights song "We Shall Overcome." But at the same time, the Beach Boys were singing about school spirit and fun in the sun. The early conflict about military involvement in Vietnam was sung about in 1965 by Barry McGuire in the discouraging song "Eve of Destruction" and by Barry Sadler in the patriotic song "Ballad of the Green Beret." A few years later, a gradual shift in mood became evident in Dylan's song "John Wesley Harding" which suggested calmer questions and possible answers even as Country Joe and the Fish protested loudly against the draft. Finally, music as a mirror of the political and social process in America was highlighted at Woodstock, New York where half a million young people came together in 1969 to spend three days listening to songs that spanned the decade. This event, like John Lennon's public performance of "Give Peace a Chance" in November 1969, was a symbol of the desire for unity within a time of turmoil. Woodstock was a display of hope in days of rage.

33. A conclusion that can be drawn from this passage is that what we view as historical events are

(1) not simply isolated names and dates
(2) ignored by young people
(3) subjects of controversy
(4) highly symbolic
(5) really symptoms of larger cycles

34. According to this passage, much of the music of the sixties might be regarded as

(1) a symptom of political apathy
(2) empty-headed rebellion
(3) a reaffirmation of some basic American ideals
(4) harmful to moral and physical health
(5) a return to normalcy

35. In addition to reflecting social and political values, the music of the sixties most likely

(1) influenced the values of American youth
(2) brought the Vietnam conflict to an end
(3) created a generation of drug addicts
(4) showed adults the error of their ways
(5) returned to the concept of innocence

36. Information in this passage indicates that the American youth of the sixties were

(1) taking too many drugs
(2) politically aware
(3) self-absorbed
(4) against the Vietnam War
(5) uninterested in social issues

37. During Ronald Reagan's last days as president, Soviet leader Mikhail Gorbachev visited New York. He is the first Soviet party official to do so since 1960 when Nikita Khrushchev banged his shoe on a desk at the United Nations General Assembly. Gorbachev's visit was most likely

(1) a gesture of apology for the previous insult
(2) a salute to the political power of the presidency
(3) an appeal for financial assistance
(4) an act of hostility
(5) a gesture to promote good will between nations

It is all too easy to think of history as being about times that are dead and gone or as lists of names and dates. But the events that are recorded as America's history were the results of real people doing real things on a daily basis. What we call history is more than a written record of the past; it is the way people in the present view what has happened and what is happening now. Although our history consists of everything that everyone has done, historians highlight what seems most significant in terms of long-lasting effect.

It has been said that history repeats itself, that history is a continuous development from necessity to freedom, and that history is always written wrong and so must always be rewritten. Whichever view of history one may take, the important thing is to consider how the past, essentially yesterday's news, affects the actions of those people living in the present.

38. According to the passage, historians describe history

(1) as random events
(2) from many points of view
(3) as unrelated events
(4) as unimportant
(5) as a record of people's mistakes

39. The suggestion "no one was listening the first time" might be a reason why history

(1) is about the past
(2) must be rewritten
(3) affects the modern world
(4) repeats itself
(5) is a continuous process

40. A person says, "Oh, I knew about that a long time ago. That's yesterday's news." What does this comment suggest about the historical importance of today's events?

(1) They are less important than what happened yesterday.
(2) Historians are more interested in the present than the past.
(3) Current events eventually become part of the historical record.
(4) Reporters of today's news are the historians of tomorrow.
(5) Nothing that happens is really important.

41. An historian recently discovered some new information about the causes of the French Revolution. This new perspective would best be described as

(1) a necessary element of freedom
(2) history being rewritten
(3) history repeating itself
(4) a record of people's mistakes
(5) arrival at the truth

42. Adlai Stevenson's comment, "We can chart our future clearly and wisely only when we know the path which has led to the present," is best supported by which of the following ideas suggested in the passage?

(1) One person's interpretation of actions and their consequences will probably be limited.
(2) Historians sometimes discover that other historians were wrong.
(3) History is more than names and dates.
(4) History is about people and not events.
(5) The past affects the lives of people in the present.

43. Which of the following pairs provides the best example of history repeating itself?

(1) the Revolutionary War and the Civil War
(2) abolition of slavery and the defeat of the Equal Rights Amendment
(3) the assassination of Lincoln and the assassination of Kennedy
(4) reconstruction in the South and the restoration of the downtown areas in major cities
(5) the election of Calvin Coolidge and the election of George Bush

Items 44–47 refer to the following passage.

When Franklin D. Roosevelt became president, the nation was still suffering from economic troubles. Within a very short time, Roosevelt created the New Deal by proposing legislation concerning federal economies, unemployment relief, and limits on stock buying. He created so many agencies that they were referred to by initials rather than by name: NRA (National Recovery Administration), AAA (Agricultural Adjustment Administration), FERA (Federal Emergency Relief Administration), CCC (Civilian Conservation Corps), HOLC (Home Owners Loan Corporation), TVA (Tennessee Valley Authority), PWA (Public Works Administration), and WPA (Works Progress Administration). Most of the New Deal programs approached the problems of poverty and inefficiency by instituting firm government control over the financial actions of Americans. The Civilian Conservation Corps and the Works Progress Administration created government funded jobs for over nine million workers. The National Recovery Act (ruled unconstitutional in 1935) required businesses to set up rules for fair competition. Farmers were paid for *not* growing crops, thus raising the prices for their products. The Tennessee Valley Authority built dams that controlled floods and produced electricity. It also promoted wildlife preserves and conservation of natural resources. The most lasting act was the Social Security Act, which was the federal insurance plan that required workers and employers to contribute to a retirement fund. These plans were fairly successful in aiding the nation's recovery, but eventually most of the New Deal ended because some people felt that government had become too powerful.

44. The main objective of the New Deal was to

    (1) save human and natural resources
    (2) extend the power of the presidency
    (3) improve working conditions
    (4) halt unemployment
    (5) stop unethical business practices

45. Which of the following does not explain the belief that the government had gained too much power?

    (1) regulation of business practices
    (2) interference in agriculture
    (3) production of electricity for the Tennessee Valley
    (4) mandatory worker contribution to Social Security
    (5) mandatory employer contribution to Social Security

46. Why might some people have given the lighthearted nickname of "alphabet soup" to the programs of the New Deal?

    (1) The programs were easy to memorize.
    (2) The programs were known by many initials.
    (3) None of the projects were successful.
    (4) The plans were regarded as childish.
    (5) The New Deal projects were intended for the health of the nation.

47. Which of the following facts from the passage might groups opposed to the New Deal have used in support of the argument that the programs were a drain on the federal budget?

    (1) Wildlife conservation was part of the TVA.
    (2) Social Security taxes were mandatory.
    (3) The NRA was ruled unconstitutional.
    (4) Millions of workers were paid by the government.
    (5) The prices of crops rose.

Answers begin on page 97.

Directions: Choose the one best answer for each item below.

Items 1–2 refer to the following graph.

Geographical Distribution of Development Aid 1986–87 (In Percent)

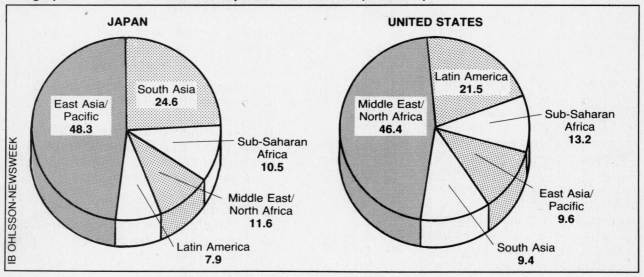

1. According to the graph, which of the following is true about the distribution of Japanese development aid in 1986–1987?

   (1) Japan provided more total aid than the United States.
   (2) Distribution of aid is concentrated in Asia.
   (3) The cash amount Japan distributed to South Asia was greater than the cash amount from the United States.
   (4) Japan's contributions are increasing each year.
   (5) Japan distributes a greater percentage to Sub-Saharan Africa than does the United States.

2. It can be inferred from the graph that

   (1) Asian nations need aid more than African nations
   (2) the United States and Japan are in direct competition
   (3) both the United States and Japan are concerned about developing nations
   (4) the donations by the United States are linked to oil production
   (5) Latin America needs less aid than South Asia

Items 3–6 refer to the following passage.

Recent experience makes it clear that economists do not have all the answers to the many and varied economic issues and questions we confront both personally and as members of the larger socioeconomic system. Here are two examples. Although economists believe they now have the knowledge and tools to prevent massive economic depressions such as the one that occurred in the 1930s, much remains to be learned about how to moderate inflation while still holding down the rate of unemployment. And the issue of what the extent of the government's role in our economy should be remains unresolved.

There are several reasons why answers to the problems economists confront are not always found. Economic systems are complex and defy easy comprehension. Moreover, our ability to know exactly how effectively the economy and its components function is often limited by the difficulty of obtaining accurate and timely measurements of economic activity. Finally, a variety of unanticipated political and social events affects economic activity and makes accurate prediction of the results of economic decisions very difficult. Unlike the situation in the physical sciences, carefully controlled experiments are difficult to undertake in economics.

3. The author is suggesting that economic prediction is difficult because

(1) the experiments often go wrong
(2) the instruments of economics are inaccurate
(3) the quantity of people is often unknown
(4) no real answers can be found
(5) depression gets to all of us

4. Another problem that illustrates the complexity of economic systems is

(1) having to balance a checkbook
(2) knowing how to moderate inflation while holding down unemployment
(3) determining the role of government in the economy
(4) that economists personally confront economic questions
(5) knowing how to balance the national budget without additional taxation

5. Which of the following is an opinion held by the author?

(1) Economists don't have all the answers.
(2) Economists can prevent economic depressions.
(3) Economists are members of a socioeconomic system.
(4) A massive depression occurred in the 1930's.
(5) Carefully controlled experiments can be conducted in the physical sciences.

6. The information in this passage supports the conclusion that the study of economics is

(1) limited to understanding patterns of buying and selling
(2) highly accurate
(3) not as important as we had previously thought
(4) based on more than just financial data
(5) the most complex of the social sciences

Items 7–8 refer to the following cartoon.

the small society   by Bill Yates

WHAT'S A FEDERAL DEFICIT?

A FEDERAL DEFICIT MEANS THROWING GOOD MONEY WE HAVEN'T GOT AFTER BAD MONEY WE NEVER HAD—

Bill Yates 3-7

7. The cartoon suggests that the federal deficit is

(1) a joking matter
(2) a serious problem
(3) something to ask your father about
(4) under mafia control
(5) easily resolved

8. The message of the cartoon is based on a reference to

(1) careful budgeting
(2) analytical questioning
(3) reckless gambling
(4) the greater good
(5) rational expenditure

Items 9–12 refer to the following definitions.

sole proprietorship—a business owned and operated by one person who receives all profits and is responsible for all debts

partnership—a business owned by two or more people who share the profits and responsibility for any debts

corporation—a business that is a legal entity, distinct from its owners, which acts as one body. Owners purchase shares of stock in the corporation. Share owners are called stockholders and are not legally liable for the business's debts.

9. After fifteen years of being partners with Mr. Allen in a pottery business, Mrs. Peters has decided to open her own business. To dissolve the partnership, she should

    (1) refuse to pay any of the pottery business's debts
    (2) put a notice in the paper declaring she is no longer responsible for any of Mr. Allen's debts
    (3) sell Mr. Allen her part of the business
    (4) simply establish sole proprietorship of her own pottery business
    (5) quit working with Mr. Allen

10. One major problem for people starting their own businesses is most likely

    (1) having to set their own hours
    (2) making all the profit
    (3) finding a market for their business
    (4) getting a large loan from a bank
    (5) deciding which accounting method to use

11. Which of the following would most likely happen if one shareholder in a corporation died?

    (1) The corporation would be dissolved.
    (2) The shares would automatically be divided among the other stockholders.
    (3) The ownership of the shares would be transferred to any heirs, who could either keep or sell them.
    (4) The other stockholders would be liable for the shareholder's debts.
    (5) The corporation could not function until the shares were sold to someone else.

12. Which of the following statements is best supported by the definitions?

    (1) The establishment and management of a corporation is more complex than that of a partnership.
    (2) A partnership is a more profitable type of business organization than a sole proprietorship.
    (3) The transfer of stock within a corporation is a time-consuming process.
    (4) A stockholder is never at any financial risk.
    (5) A business owned by a sole proprietor can be sold more easily than one owned in partnership.

Two important economic principles are the laws of supply and demand. The law of supply is that as the price of a product or service increases, the supplier usually wants to provide more to the consumer. The law of demand is that as prices decrease, the consumer usually will want to buy more.

13. Which of the following is not an example of the law of demand?

(1) As gasoline prices rise, people drive less.

(2) A local supermarket sells out of the bread it has put on sale.

(3) Automobile dealers are lowering their prices and offering cash rebates in order to increase sales.

(4) A two-pack-a-day smoker continues the habit even though the price of cigarettes goes up.

(5) Sales of personal computers increase steadily as they become more affordable to the average household.

14. When a note card manufacturer notices that retail outlets continue to order the same amounts after the wholesale price is raised from $.60 to $.75, the manufacturer will most likely

(1) lower prices again to sell even more cards

(2) increase the wholesale price again

(3) continue to produce the same number of cards to sell at $.75 each

(4) manufacture fewer cards

(5) find more outlets and make more cards

Items 15–18 refer to the following graph.

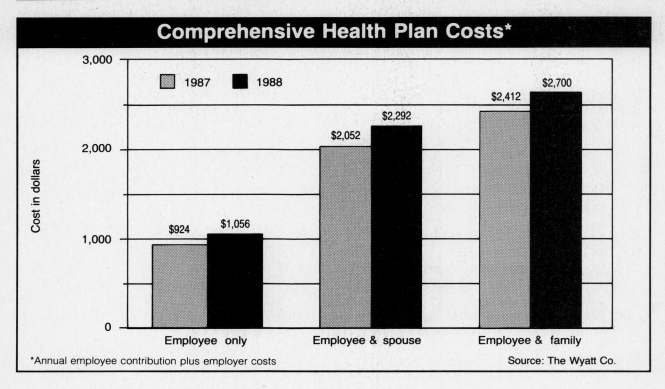

Comprehensive Health Plan Costs*

*Annual employee contribution plus employer costs

Source: The Wyatt Co.

15. According to this graph, annual comprehensive health plan costs in 1988 were

   (1) almost double that of 1987
   (2) at least 10% higher than in 1987
   (3) paid mainly by the employer
   (4) paid mainly by the employee
   (5) not worth the health care actually provided

16. If the cost of group health insurance plans continues to rise, employers most likely will

   (1) increase the percentage of their contributions
   (2) decrease the percentage of their contributions
   (3) encourage their employees to stay healthy
   (4) stop offering health insurance benefits
   (5) hire fewer employees

17. The rise in insurance costs is best explained by

   (1) an increase in the cost of medical treatment
   (2) an increase in the number of accidental death insurance claims
   (3) the reluctance of insurance companies to settle claims
   (4) a national increase in the number of people needing medical attention
   (5) the growing shortage of nursing personnel

18. The information in this graph supports the conclusion that

   (1) doctors' fees are much too high
   (2) health insurance is a necessary benefit
   (3) the cost increase in health care plans is excessive
   (4) employees should be given salary increases of 10%
   (5) insurance for employee and spouse is more cost-effective than for employee and family

At the same time production does remain important and urgent for its effect on economic security. When men are unemployed, society does not miss the goods they do not produce. The loss here is marginal. But the men who are without work do miss the income they no longer earn. Here the effect is not marginal. It involves all or a large share of the men's earnings and hence all or a large share of what they are able to buy. And, we note, high and stable production is the broad foundation of the economic security of virtually every other group—of farmers, white-collar workers, and both large businessmen and small. The depression also remains the major uncovered risk of the modern large corporation. It is for reasons of economic security that we must produce at capacity.

19. Which of the following proverbs best summarizes the author's assumption about goods that are not produced?

   (1) Absence makes the heart grow fonder.
   (2) Out of sight, out of mind.
   (3) You don't miss your water 'til your well runs dry.
   (4) Better late than never.
   (5) Don't cut off your nose to spite your face.

20. According to the passage, a low level of goods production would not result in which of the following?

   (1) unemployment
   (2) less spending
   (3) an unstable economy
   (4) loss of personal income
   (5) a less capitalistic society

21. If an index of low productivity is the need to import certain consumer goods, in which of the following areas does the United States most likely have the highest productivity?

   (1) wheat
   (2) automobiles
   (3) televisions
   (4) oil
   (5) VCRs

22. Which of the following conclusions is best supported by the passage?

   (1) Too many people are unemployed.
   (2) The product itself is less important than the production of it.
   (3) Our society is too concerned with material goods.
   (4) The policies of modern corporations are leading to another depression.
   (5) Capacity of production will solve all economic problems.

23. The cartoon suggests that

   (1) savings and loan institutions are charitable organizations

   (2) people can use savings and loan deposits as tax write-offs

   (3) savings and loan institutions are financially insecure

   (4) modern banking procedures are inadequate for today's economy

   (5) the savings and loan institution is available for all financial transactions

24. When using the phrase "deposit or donation," the cartoonist expects the reader to be familiar with

   (1) a teller's usual question of "deposit or withdrawal"

   (2) a teller's request for identification

   (3) a loan officer's request for collateral

   (4) the offer of a free toaster for opening a new account

   (5) the customer's confusion about how a savings and loan institution works

WALL STREET'S RECESSION

25. The cartoon is based on the assumption that most people

   (1) are interested in the investment market

   (2) know that Wall Street refers to a major financial district

   (3) know that Wall Street is in New York

   (4) know that Wall Street is in Chicago

   (5) can recognize the Empire State Building

26. The conclusion that can be drawn from the cartoon is that

   (1) Wall Street no longer exists

   (2) activity on Wall Street is no longer brisk

   (3) there are dirty politics in the stock market

   (4) city streets need to be cleaned up

   (5) the stock market has collapsed

Items 27–28 refer to the following chart.

The Economy

Gross National Product In billions, annual rate	4th Q'88 $4,033.4	3rd Q'88 $4,009.4	Year ago $3,870.0
Real G.N.P. growth Annual %, '82 dollars	2.4	2.5	4.2
Corporate after-tax profits In billions, annual rate	4th Q'88 $173.9	3rd Q'88 $169.1	Year ago $144.2
Plant, equipment spending In billions, annual rate	4th Q'88 $443.7	3rd Q'88 $436.0	Year ago $398.0
Industrial production Percentage change	March 0.6	Feb. 0.0	Year ago 0.3
Housing starts Thousands, annual rate	March 1,400	Feb. 1,500	Year ago 1,540
New orders for durable goods Manufacturers, billions	Feb. $123.70	Jan. $128.06	Year ago $111.40
Sales at retail outlets In billions	March $139.4	Feb. $138.2	Year ago $130.7
Employment In thousands	March 118,820	Feb. 118,537	Year ago 115,839
Unemployment In thousands Rate, in percent	 6,128 4.9	 6,328 5.1	 6,801 5.5

27. According to the chart, which of the following has increased during the last year?

(1) unemployment
(2) housing starts
(3) the rate of gross national product growth
(4) retail sales
(5) consumer prices

28. The increase in orders of durable goods is most likely a result of

(1) improved sales techniques
(2) more people having money to spend
(3) a national rejection of disposable products
(4) a new trend in advertising
(5) more people moving into new homes

Items 29–30 refer to the following cartoon.

"GREAT! THE BAGGAGE HANDLERS BROKE ALL THE SIGNS!"

29. It can be inferred from this cartoon that

(1) an airline workers' union was picketing
(2) this worker is tired of the strike
(3) strikers need to reorganize the picket lines
(4) the cartoonist is in favor of the airlines
(5) the couple will not be able to book a flight

30. Which conclusion can be drawn from the cartoon?

(1) Everyone is angry with the airlines.
(2) The strike is about to end.
(3) Not all airline workers are in favor of the strike.
(4) The issues involved cannot be resolved.
(5) Striking is not allowed by airline unions.

Items 31–34 refer to the following graphs.

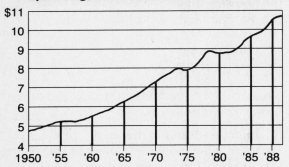

Inflation-Adjusted Per Capita Personal Spending; in Thousands of 1982 Dollars

Source: Commerce Department, Bureau of Labor Statistics

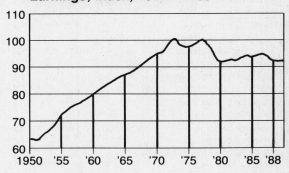

Inflation-Adjusted Average Hourly Earnings; Index, 1977 = 100

31. From the information on the graphs, it seems that people will

    (1) be very budget-conscious
    (2) pay close attention to the inflation rate
    (3) always live beyond their means
    (4) often spend money no matter what their wages are
    (5) spend more money as they get older

32. The decrease in average hourly earnings is most likely a reflection of

    (1) a decrease in the minimum wage
    (2) an increase in the minimum wage
    (3) a depression
    (4) a change in the level of productivity
    (5) increased taxation

33. If the wage trend shown in the graphs continues, the next generation will most likely

    (1) have a lower standard of living than we do now
    (2) live better than we do now
    (3) live about the same way as they always have
    (4) spend more money than we do now
    (5) live in poverty

34. The information in the graphs best supports the idea that

    (1) the new tax system is not working
    (2) inflation does not affect spending and earning in the same way
    (3) life is getting better all the time
    (4) increased spending results in increased earning
    (5) the economy has been stable for almost forty years

Items 35–36 refer to the following passage.

Production of any product or service requires three basic ingredients. The first of these, labor, is the human effort involved. The second ingredient is capital. Capital, or money, also includes all the other products necessary to produce something. The third ingredient includes the supplies or resources provided by nature.

35. An important natural resource for the production of furniture is

(1) a carpenter
(2) a hammer
(3) lumber
(4) plastic
(5) cloth

36. Which of the following businesses would be most likely to spend the largest percentage of money on natural resources for its production of goods or services?

(1) a small photographic chemical manufacturer
(2) a retail liquor store
(3) a publishing house
(4) a housekeeping service
(5) an athletic shoe manufacturer

Items 37–38 refer to the following cartoon.

"Yes, this is the dotty old lady of the house, but no I don't want to buy any of your penny stocks."

37. The cartoonist is expressing the opinion that

(1) some investment firms try to take advantage of senior citizens
(2) older people are not interested in investments
(3) not even cheap stocks justify rudeness
(4) penny stocks are not a wise investment
(5) investment transactions should never be conducted over the telephone

38. The cartoonist is most likely

(1) an advocate of penny stocks
(2) against the sale of penny stocks
(3) a financial expert
(4) an advocate of consumer protection laws
(5) against consumer protection laws

Answers begin on page 100.

Chapter 4 Political Science ❑

Directions: Choose the <u>one best answer</u> for each item below.

<u>Items 1–4</u> refer to the following passage.

Our dependency upon others makes us dependent on government. Each of us is a specialist in just a few areas of life; we are mechanics, farmers, teachers, homemakers, whatever. As a result we must depend on specialists in other economic areas for most of the goods and services we need.

To ensure that we will not be endangered by that dependency, we turn to government. Why endangered? Because almost all the specialists on whom we depend have no moral or legal obligation to us, aside from whatever they voluntarily assume or government requires. Primarily, they relate to us in an impersonal way, through money and profit. People who are bound by feelings of affection or friendship are most likely to treat each other fairly and honestly. A producer who never sees the consumer is less likely to be concerned about the individual who buys or uses his products. In this impersonal economic world in which we live, the drive to achieve success, measured by money or prestige, leads some individuals to ignore the safety and health needs of those who depend on them for goods and services. Not all producers, manufacturers, or service providers are irresponsible, of course, but enough of them are to make life sufficiently uncertain and dangerous for the rest of us, were it not for government.

1. One of the United States government agencies that exists to ensure honest treatment of citizens is

   (1) NATO
   (2) the United Nations
   (3) the Food and Drug Administration
   (4) the United States Postal Service
   (5) the CIA

2. In which of the following ways does the government ensure the protection of its citizens?

   (1) by passing laws
   (2) by issuing press releases
   (3) through proclamations
   (4) with investigating committees
   (5) by conducting surveys

3. According to the passage, a primary function of government is to

   (1) impose economic order on society
   (2) guarantee liberty
   (3) take care of the farmers
   (4) make sure individuals are not dependent on others
   (5) ensure an individual's complete independence

4. Which of the following best supports the necessity of having a government in today's world?

   (1) Most people don't have anyone they can really trust.
   (2) Most families live too far apart to rely on each other.
   (3) Most individuals are not self-sufficient.
   (4) The market economy is uncertain and dangerous.
   (5) An impersonal world breeds deception.

See Also ▶ Social Studies pages 168–217
Complete Preparation pages 303–319

Items 5–8 refer to the following passage.

The theory of democracy is based on four principles. First, every individual has value. Second, all individuals are entitled to freedom of choice. Third, there is no absolute truth. Fourth, all individuals are equal.

5. The statement that all individuals are equal means that

   (1) everyone has the same abilities
   (2) all people should be given the same respect
   (3) given equal opportunities, all individuals can achieve the same goals
   (4) handicapped people should not be given special concessions
   (5) people want the same things

6. According to the passage, the idea of democracy rests on

   (1) proven facts
   (2) firm ground
   (3) a set of beliefs
   (4) inalienable rights
   (5) self-evident truths

7. According to these principles of democracy, people should be able to

   (1) do whatever seems best at the time
   (2) discriminate against someone different from themselves
   (3) impose their beliefs on others
   (4) question the validity of a law
   (5) prohibit the general use of something they don't like

8. Which of the following was influenced the least by the principles outlined in the passage?

   (1) the Bill of Rights
   (2) the Declaration of Independence
   (3) the separation of church and state in the United States
   (4) civil rights legislation
   (5) the State of the Union address

Items 9–10 refer to the following cartoon.

Reprinted with special permission of King Features Syndicate, Inc.

9. Which of the following statements best summarizes the cartoonist's opinion of political candidates?

   (1) They employ large support staffs.
   (2) None of them should hire gag writers.
   (3) They don't seem to be able to speak for themselves.
   (4) Their speeches don't always make much sense.
   (5) They should give more credit to the quality of their speech writers.

10. According to the implication of the cartoon, with which of the following statements might the cartoonist be most likely to agree?

   (1) Debate briefings are a waste of time.
   (2) Humor has no place in politics.
   (3) Speech writers should not be employed in a campaign.
   (4) Political debates are conducted like television shows.
   (5) Political speech writers are too specialized.

Items 11–14 refer to the following passage about the Sixth Amendment to the Constitution.

In all criminal prosecutions, the accused shall enjoy the right to a speedy and public trial by an impartial jury of the State and district wherein the crime shall have been committed, which district shall have been previously ascertained by law, and to be informed of the nature and cause of the accusation; to be confronted with the witnesses against him; to have compulsory process for obtaining witnesses in his favor, and to have the Assistance of Counsel for his defense.

11. Under this law, a poor person who is arrested for a crime is entitled to

    (1) one free phone call
    (2) bail provided by the state
    (3) a public defender
    (4) be tried within a week
    (5) a free meal

12. For which of the following reasons is it more difficult to get an impartial jury today than it was when the amendment was written?

    (1) Modern society is more opinionated than the colonials were.
    (2) People today are a lot more streetwise.
    (3) The news media often publicizes the details of a crime before it comes to trial.
    (4) People today know more about criminal psychology.
    (5) Juries are in a hurry to end the trial, and they make snap judgments.

13. The best title for this amendment is

    (1) Liberty for All
    (2) To Bear False Witness
    (3) Prevention of Unfair Arrest
    (4) The Trial Process
    (5) A Fair Trial

14. The writers of this amendment most likely intended to provide against

    (1) an indecisive jury
    (2) trial of an innocent person
    (3) unjust imprisonment
    (4) lengthy court proceedings
    (5) dull trials

Items 15–16 are based on the following cartoon.

You did your patriotic duty? You mean you voted?...

Naw. I responded to a poll......

Mike Luckovich
Times-Picayune

15. The cartoonist is expressing the opinion that

    (1) opinion polls are as important as votes
    (2) the man did his patriotic duty
    (3) opinion polls are mistakenly regarded as important
    (4) people who respond to polls will also vote
    (5) polls should take the place of voting

16. The cartoonist most likely thinks that

    (1) some Americans do not really understand the political process
    (2) Americans always do their patriotic duty
    (3) opinion polls will elect a politician
    (4) opinion polls are worthless
    (5) patriots always respond to opinion polls

17. The United States traditionally has operated on a two-party political system. Recently, however, third-party nominees have shown up on ballots in major elections. This situation suggests that

    (1) the political system is falling apart
    (2) the third party will gain more support
    (3) not all voters are satisfied with the two major parties
    (4) the two major parties will change their policies
    (5) the ballot system is being abused

18. A tobacco company sends paid agents to Washington, D.C. to lobby in Congress against raising taxes on cigarettes. This is an example of

    (1) unfair trade
    (2) a pressure group at work
    (3) an attack against antismoking campaigns
    (4) unfair taxation
    (5) corruption in the legislature

19. The winds of political change were blowing in China during the spring of 1989 when thousands of students in Beijing and Shanghai protested against the government. It was evident that the students wanted

    (1) a Western-style democracy
    (2) a return to hardline communism
    (3) to put an end to authoritarianism
    (4) to have a say in how the government is run
    (5) to overthrow the existing Communist party

Items **20-23** refer to the following definitions.

traditional authority—a power based on ancient custom, the claim to which is usually based on inheritance or birthright

legal-rational authority—a power granted by rules and laws that define the obligations of the officials

charismatic authority—a power that occurs because of the unique characteristics of a specific leader

20. Which one of the following political figures can most likely be called a charismatic leader?

   (1) Queen Elizabeth II
   (2) President George Bush
   (3) Ayatollah Khomeini
   (4) General Secretary Mikhail Gorbachev
   (5) Governor Michael Dukakis

21. Which of the following statements best explains why charismatic authority is an unstable basis for government?

   (1) Charismatic figures are unstable personalities.
   (2) Power is centered on an individual who could fail or die.
   (3) The followers of a charismatic leader are fanatics.
   (4) Charismatic leaders often head revolutions.
   (5) A personality-based authority will clash with a legal-rational authority.

22. Under which of the following systems would traditional authority be most likely to occur?

   (1) a democratic government
   (2) a socialist republic
   (3) a Communist state
   (4) a monarchy
   (5) a dictatorship

23. The definitions support the conclusion that in the United States an official's power is derived from

   (1) the office itself
   (2) personal characteristics
   (3) tradition
   (4) social status
   (5) loyal supporters

Items 24–27 refer to the following passage.

In seeking to lighten the President's burden, we would do well to recall the warning of Woodrow Wilson: "Men of ordinary physique and discretion cannot be Presidents and live, if the strain be not somehow relieved. We shall be obliged always to be picking our chief magistrates from among wise and prudent athletes—a small class." At the same time, we should also recall that a long list of routine tasks, each of which appears "nonessential" when viewed by itself, may well add up to an inspired performance of a great function of state. The President cannot be a successful Chief of State if he turns all the little ceremonies and visits over to the Vice-President. He cannot lead Congress if he is unwilling to spend hours listening to Congressmen. And he cannot be a vigorous Commander in Chief unless he studies the defense budget item by item. For him as for all of us there is no final escape from hard and pedestrian labor. And as the gentlemen of Congress warned in the law of 1950 I have just mentioned: "Nothing contained herein shall relieve the President of his responsibility" for the acts of those "designated by him to perform functions." As Mr. Truman would say, the President may pass the details but not the buck.

24. The law of 1950 that the author refers to is most likely one that

    (1) limits the responsibilities of the president
    (2) adds more duties to the office of the president
    (3) allows the president to pass the buck
    (4) permits the president to delegate some duties to aides
    (5) relieves the president of all nonessential routine tasks

25. According to the passage, the duties of the president of the United States are

    (1) many and complex
    (2) very easy
    (3) being taken over by the vice president
    (4) routine
    (5) inspiring

26. According to the initial quotation by Woodrow Wilson, the best candidate for president would most likely have to resemble which of the following cartoon characters?

    (1) Daffy Duck
    (2) Fred Flintstone
    (3) Bugs Bunny
    (4) Superman
    (5) the Hulk

27. The author of the passage would be most likely to agree with the idea that

    (1) executives should only be concerned with the overall picture
    (2) an understanding of a part helps in understanding the whole
    (3) small ceremonies should not be duties of the president
    (4) if you take care of yourself, the details will take care of themselves
    (5) the vice president should not perform any of the president's duties

Items 28–31 refer to the following map.

Presidential Election, 1800

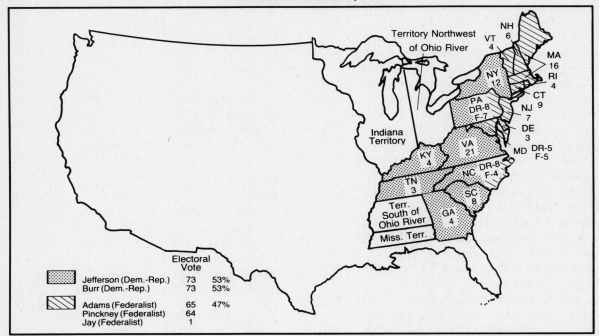

Electoral Vote		
Jefferson (Dem.-Rep.)	73	53%
Burr (Dem.-Rep.)	73	53%
Adams (Federalist)	65	47%
Pinckney (Federalist)	64	
Jay (Federalist)	1	

28. According to the map, how many states split their vote in the 1800 election?

    (1) three
    (2) four
    (3) five
    (4) six
    (5) seven

29. If the candidate receiving the most votes would become president, and the candidate with the second highest vote would become vice president, why did the Federalist party cast one vote for Jay?

    (1) Only one state electoral voter disliked Pickney.
    (2) It was a sympathy vote.
    (3) It was a strategy to guarantee Adams as president if the Federalist party had a majority.
    (4) The Maryland Federalists couldn't agree on which candidate was best.
    (5) Jay was not considered to be presidential material.

30. The information on the map best supports the conclusion that

    (1) a two-party system does not work
    (2) Adams had little support in New England
    (3) electoral votes do not reflect the popular vote
    (4) electoral votes are more efficient than popular votes
    (5) Indiana didn't have a vote because it wasn't a state

31. Which of the following cannot be determined from this map?

    (1) how many electoral votes each state had
    (2) how many votes each candidate received
    (3) who actually became president
    (4) which states participated in the election
    (5) who lost the election

The burning of draft cards or American flags involves direct violation of law. Laws forbidding the burning or desecration of the national flag have existed for many years, and it is hardly likely that anyone would seriously contest their constitutionality or legality. In the case of draft cards, however, it has been vigorously urged that the federal law prohibiting mutilation or burning of draft cards serves no real purpose and was recently enacted by the Congress merely to punish dissent. For this reason, it is said, the law is an unconstitutional burden on the right of free speech. Therefore, it is argued, the draft card burning should not be held to involve a violation of law. A case involving this question is awaiting decision by the Supreme Court and I cannot comment upon it. But the point that I make is that if the law forbidding the burning of a draft card is held to be constitutional and valid, the fact that the card is burned as a result of noble and constitutionally protected motives is no help to the offender.

32. The author of the passage is most likely

   (1) an antiwar protester
   (2) an average citizen
   (3) a reporter
   (4) a judge
   (5) an opponent of the Constitution

33. At the time the passage was written, the act of burning a draft card was

   (1) acceptable as an assertion of a constitutional right
   (2) illegal even if done as an assertion of a constitutional right
   (3) not punishable by law
   (4) upheld by the Constitution
   (5) not regarded as an act of dissent

34. When the Supreme Court ruled in 1989 that burning the American flag in political protest is legal under the Constitution, it contradicted this author's opinion that

   (1) political protest is unconstitutional
   (2) the validity of a law depends on its constitutional validity
   (3) the Constitution specifically forbids the burning of the American flag
   (4) freedom of speech does not apply to political dissent
   (5) laws forbidding the desecration of the flag would not be challenged

35. Jim Crow laws that supported racial segregation are examples of laws that

   (1) have constitutional validity
   (2) were abolished because they were unconstitutional
   (3) serve no real purpose
   (4) punished dissent
   (5) violated the right of free speech

Items 36–37 refer to the following graphs.

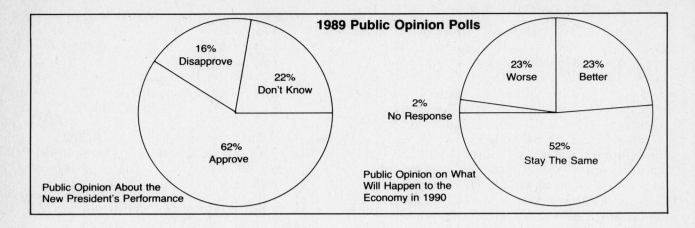

36. The graphs support the idea that

    (1) public approval of the new president's performance does not necessarily mean the public believes he can improve the economy
    (2) people who approve of the president's performance also believe the economy will stay as it is
    (3) some people insist on seeing the negative side of everything
    (4) improvement of the nation's economy depends on the president's performance
    (5) opinion polls are an accurate reflection of political facts

37. Which of the following best characterizes those people who neither approved nor disapproved of the president's performance?

    (1) outspoken
    (2) not interested
    (3) the hole in the wall gang
    (4) the ugly Americans
    (5) the criminal element

Items 38–39 refer to the following passage.

In July 1971, the first national women's political caucus met to define women's issues that could be affected through political channels. These concerns were presented the next year at the Democratic convention, where 35% of the delegates were women.

38. Which of the following is true according to the passage?

    (1) Women were not politically active until 1972.
    (2) The Republican party does not believe women should have a role in politics.
    (3) Women realized that there is power in organization.
    (4) The national caucus sponsored the Democratic women delegates.
    (5) The caucus provides campaign support for women of both major parties.

39. Which of the following subjects most likely was not a topic at the first women's caucus?

    (1) child care centers
    (2) the appointment of women to cabinet posts
    (3) the Equal Rights Amendment
    (4) sexual harrassment on the job
    (5) gun control

40. The original American filibusters were a group of people who attacked a Latin American country with which their own country was at peace. They wasted time and money on a political move that made no sense. Today the word *filibuster* refers to a prolonged and often irrelevant speech presented by a representative or senator. Legislators deliver filibusters in order to

(1) impress the public with legislative rhetoric
(2) support military adventures overseas
(3) delay business by disrupting regular procedures
(4) be patriotic to their constituents
(5) explain their positions to the news media

Items 41–44 refer to the following passage by the U.S. Secretary of Education.

"As a nation, our educational performance is merely average," Cavazos said. "People are still willing, apparently, to accept that we're not doing well and can't compete."

If educational progress has stagnated, the Education Department's chart shows the same cannot be said of per-pupil spending. The national average was $3,977 per student in 1987, up from $3,165 in 1982, calculated in constant dollars—a 26 percent hike.

"We are already spending more money per student than our major foreign competitors, Japan and Germany. And yet our students consistently fall behind the competition in competitive testing," Cavazos said. "Money alone is not the answer to our education deficit."

Cavazos said he would write to state school chiefs, governors and school board presidents and urge them to adopt specific goals such as boosting high school graduation rates to 90 percent and cutting in half the number of children who fail a grade. He said states and districts should issue annual reports on their progress toward such goals.

Specifically, the department's chart shows that national scores on the Scholastic Aptitude Test fell from an average of 906 to 904 (on a scale of 400 to 1,600) from 1987 to 1988. Fourteen of the 22 states in which the SAT is the dominant college entrance exam registered declines.

41. According to the passage, spending more money on education has

(1) resulted in a lowered national SAT average
(2) benefited the students
(3) drained the national deficit
(4) put us in competition with Japan and West Germany
(5) made no difference

42. Cavazos believes that state participation in education could

(1) cause parental outrage
(2) assist in upgrading test scores
(3) lead to academic tyranny
(4) add more money to the education budget
(5) cause more children to fail

43. The passage supports the opinion that

(1) the average American student is not very intelligent
(2) responsibility for education should be shifted from the local to the national level
(3) going to school doesn't guarantee an education
(4) high school diplomas aren't worth the paper they are written on
(5) SAT scores should no longer be used as college entrance requirements

44. Cavazos bases his argument that the American educational performance is only average on

(1) statistics about per-pupil spending
(2) the percentage of students graduating from high school
(3) college entrance requirements
(4) a comparison with foreign countries
(5) people's acceptance of the situation

---

45. After World War II, "right-to-work" laws were passed by twenty states, barring labor unions from requiring membership as a condition of employment. Because labor unions have had a major role in American politics, these laws most likely

(1) relieved some workers of unwanted political connections
(2) increased political activity on the part of the unions
(3) increased labor union strength in the other states
(4) influenced unions to affiliate with the Democratic party
(5) led to the end of labor unions in the twenty states

46. For raising operational monies, states rely primarily on sales taxes. Cities rely primarily on property taxes. When trying to attract new businesses from other states, a major city would most likely try to offer the businesses

(1) increased sales taxes
(2) decreased sales taxes
(3) a high property tax rate
(4) a low property tax rate
(5) a break on federal income taxes

Answers begin on page 102.

Chapter 5 Behavioral Science ❏

Directions: Choose the <u>one best answer</u> for each item below.

<u>Items 1–4</u> refer to the following passage.

Knowing that a good pictorial likeness is not necessarily an exact copy of a scene as it actually appears, artists often deliberately break the rules of perspective. For example, to correct for the size distortion called for by the rules of perspective, they may draw a distant mountain larger than it would appear in a photograph. Perhaps for similar reasons, children may not at first draw objects with optical realism; they are interested in showing things in the most informative way rather than showing exactly how things look.

Do children improve further as they get older? If realism is the standard, the answer is clearly yes. For example, their figures become more complex, and they can represent depth through linear perspective. But I believe, on esthetic grounds, that children's drawings actually get worse with age.

Because preschool children are unconcerned with realism, their drawings are free, fanciful and inventive. Suns may be green, cars may float in the sky and complex, irregular forms in nature are reduced to a few regular geometric shapes. They produce simple, strong pictures that evoke the abstractions found in folk, "primitive" and contemporary art.

The older child's drawing may be more realistic, neat and precise, but, in my opinion, it is also less imaginative and less striking. Suns are now appropriately yellow and placed carefully in the corner of the pictures, and cars now rest firmly on the ground.

1. This author believes a young child's drawings are

   (1) meaningless
   (2) interesting
   (3) complex
   (4) realistic
   (5) deliberately abstract

2. Which of the following would this author enjoy the least?

   (1) an imaginative cartoon
   (2) a watercolor sketch
   (3) a coloring book
   (4) a doodle
   (5) a woodcut

3. This author most likely has the opinion that

   (1) one disadvantage to the learning process is a loss of creativity
   (2) the more realistically children draw, the more information they can convey
   (3) even very young children are concerned with the rules of perspective
   (4) the only true art is contemporary
   (5) maturity produces a more sensitive artist

4. According to the information in the passage, folk art is popular because

   (1) it is better than classical painting
   (2) its style is inventive and childlike
   (3) folk artists are more perceptive than trained artists
   (4) children like it
   (5) it breaks the rules of perspective

See Also ▶ | Social Studies Complete Preparation | pages 218–247 pages 320–336

Items 5–8 refer to the following passage.

The IQ (intelligence quotient) test is often used as a measure of intelligence, but apparently it can assess only one type of mental ability. According to a recent theory, there are three types of intelligence: componential, experiential, and contextual. Componential intelligence is the analytical or critical thinking that results in good test-taking skills scores. Experiential intelligence is less analytical but more creative, and it results in being able to put ideas together in new ways. Contextual intelligence operates more on a practical level and results in adapting well to circumstances, and in learning quickly from experience. No one type of intelligence is believed to be better than another, but recognizing the three types may help people to better understand their own strengths and weaknesses.

5. People with componential intelligence are considered to be smart by educators who traditionally have placed a high value on

   (1) new ideas
   (2) whiz kids
   (3) graduation
   (4) creativity
   (5) high test scores

6. Which of the following people is most likely to be recognized as having experiential intelligence?

   (1) an artist
   (2) a teacher
   (3) a police officer
   (4) a bartender
   (5) a typist

7. The passage supports the inference that a person with contextual intelligence

   (1) can get better grades than someone with experiential intelligence
   (2) can handle unexpected situations fairly easily
   (3) will be less successful than other people
   (4) should not go into business
   (5) would be a good editor

8. The information in the passage best explains why

   (1) some people never go to college
   (2) IQ tests have been used as a measure of intelligence
   (3) IQ tests have not always been reliable predictors of mental ability
   (4) geniuses are never very practical
   (5) psychologists are interested in IQ tests

Item 9 refers to the following passage.

Because personality traits are often passed from one family member to another, some scientists believed that abnormal behaviors such as alcoholism, sexual deviance, and criminal activity were the result of "bad blood." Today scientists believe that personality development is affected by both inherited potentials and environment.

9. Social scientists who subscribed to the theory of "bad blood" were most likely influenced by

   (1) early scientific studies on the transmission of similar genetic traits
   (2) poor home environments of their own
   (3) B.F. Skinner's belief that behavior is totally determined by environment
   (4) the discovery of germs as the cause of disease
   (5) the concept of vampirism

10. The cartoonist is suggesting that

(1) people are right to be content with how they appear to others
(2) some people need counseling more than others
(3) self-confidence can sometimes make people blind to the reasons for other people's judgments of themselves
(4) people are jealous of self-confident personalities
(5) self-doubt leads one to be suspicious of other people

11. The psychologist in the cartoon is basing his first question on the assumption that

(1) people have role models after whom they would like to pattern themselves
(2) psychologists have all the answers
(3) it is better to be someone other than yourself
(4) his client has an identity problem
(5) people can easily change their personalities

Items 12–15 refer to the following passage.

Some sociologists use a basic method of research for making discoveries and developing theories. They begin with a paradigm, or a grand model of how something works. From that, sociologists develop a statement of explanation that is not provable or testable but is essentially a belief. The theory, however, can imply an hypothesis, a testable idea.

Unfortunately, just because the hypothesis has been tested and is correct does not mean the theory the hypothesis came from is also correct. An example of this from astronomy is Ptolemy's theory that the earth was the center of the universe. In his day, the theory was impossible to prove or disprove, so he developed an hypothesis that explained the movement of the North Star. The hypothesis allowed people to predict the positions of the stars. But the movements of the planets could not be explained by the theory. Nonetheless, people maintained for centuries that the earth was the center of the universe.

12. This passage best explains why

(1) some social theories are better than others
(2) sociologists are able to analyze human interactions
(3) there is a difference between science and social science
(4) why some social theories remain popular even when they are proven wrong
(5) human behavior is so predictable

13. The statement that wars are the result of uncontrollable forces in modern society is an example of

(1) a proven hypothesis
(2) a disproven hypothesis
(3) a theory
(4) a conclusion based on an hypothesis
(5) a popular belief

14. Which of the following would be a logical hypothesis for the theory that age roles are developed by a society's attitudes, beliefs, and values?

(1) The regular employment of children is immoral.
(2) Teenagers may be rebellious because they are expected to be.
(3) Many people retire at the age of 65.
(4) A person becomes a legal adult at the age of 21.
(5) The elderly cannot handle the pressures of life.

15. Testing a sociological hypothesis is most difficult because

(1) human behavior is unpredictable
(2) there are no facts about human behavior
(3) many factors are involved in human behavior
(4) it depends on personal observation
(5) most social theories have been proven to be faulty

Items 16–17 refer to the following cartoon.

"He's a criminal lawyer...But, then, aren't they all?"

16. The main idea of the cartoon is that

(1) lawyers cannot successfully represent their clients
(2) many people don't trust lawyers
(3) people know very little about the law
(4) lawyers encourage criminal behavior
(5) lawyers are highly valued by society

17. Which of the following expressions might the women use to support their opinion?

(1) Crime doesn't pay.
(2) Birds of a feather flock together.
(3) Ignorance of the law excuses no one.
(4) A gossip is worse than a thief.
(5) Two heads are better than one.

Item 18 refers to the following diagram.

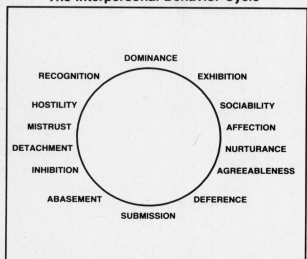

The Interpersonal Behavior Cycle

DOMINANCE
RECOGNITION
EXHIBITION
HOSTILITY
SOCIABILITY
MISTRUST
AFFECTION
DETACHMENT
NURTURANCE
INHIBITION
AGREEABLENESS
ABASEMENT
DEFERENCE
SUBMISSION

18. According to the diagram, each of the behaviors listed has

(1) a negative social impact
(2) a positive social impact
(3) an influence on other behaviors
(4) an opposite behavior
(5) a recognizable pattern

Items 19–22 refer to the following diagrams.

Key Movements Between Managers in an Office

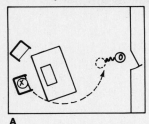
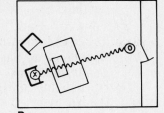

A

B

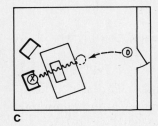
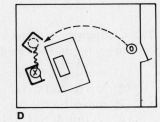

C

D

19. In diagram A, manager O most likely

(1) works for manager X
(2) oversees the work done by manager X
(3) performs the same job as manager X
(4) is trying to impress manager X
(5) is uncomfortable with manager X

20. The pattern of movements shown in the diagrams supports the opinion that communication

(1) is difficult between people who do the same job
(2) can be achieved clearly only by talking
(3) can be nonverbal
(4) is awkward in the business world
(5) is restricted by social status

21. If manager O in diagram D suddenly behaved like manager O in diagram B, it would most likely indicate that manager X

(1) had been demoted
(2) had been promoted
(3) had become more friendly with manager O
(4) had offended manager O
(5) had decided to quit

22. The diagrams not only reflect the way these managers behave toward each other, but they also suggest that in our society

(1) physical distance is an important factor
(2) offices are carefully arranged to be uncomfortable
(3) businesses are organized by the social status of the employees
(4) the business world is highly competitive
(5) managers are highly valued

23. On the Pacific island of Truk when children act inappropriately, adults would most likely say, "They don't know yet; they're only children." But in America that same behavior would most likely be corrected, perhaps with impatience. This difference suggests that Americans place a higher value on

(1) tolerance of children
(2) learning quickly
(3) adult authority
(4) talented children
(5) childhood freedom

The native peoples of the American continents had complex languages and highly developed systems of abstract thought. Over 2,000 distinct languages existed, with several occurring within one culture area. In the sub-arctic region there were two language divisions called Athapascan and Algonquian. The California area was especially rich in languages. For example, in the small region occupied by the Yana Indians, there was one basic language with four distinct dialects. The wide range of linguistic ability and sophistication is indicated by the Yanomamo Indian tribe's taboo against speaking a dead person's name, thus requiring new names to be imaginative and extraordinary in order to avoid disrespectful mention of the dead in daily conversation. Another example of this sophistication is the New York Iroquois whose complex religious structure was based on an equally developed conception of soul, unconscious, conscious, and ego, all of which needed detailed terminology.

24. The passage can be used to discredit the image of the native Americans as

(1) noble savages
(2) warriorlike
(3) peaceful
(4) skilled hunters
(5) highly spiritual

25. An example that best supports the main idea of the passage is

(1) the pottery tradition of the southwestern Pueblo Indian
(2) the writing and mathematical systems in pre-Columbian Mesoamerica
(3) the elaborate basketry of the Great Basin Shoshoni
(4) the hunting and gathering system of the Apache
(5) the nuclear family structure of the Yahgan Indians of Tierra del Fuego

26. According to the passage, complexity of language is the result of

(1) naming practices
(2) territorial divisions
(3) dialects developing within one language
(4) a complex social or cultural need
(5) a religious structure

27. The Yanamamo's naming taboo indicates a cultural

(1) respect for the spiritual
(2) emphasis on conversation
(3) dislike of death
(4) avoidance of the unpleasant
(5) misunderstanding of the power of language

Items 28–30 refer to the following passage and chart.

An anthropologist recorded the expenses for ceremonies he attended in a village in Thailand. The following chart provides information on the *bahts* (Thai currency) spent for a wedding.

Finances for a Single Wedding in Thailand

Item	Amount
Expenses	
Rice	3 sacks 1,860
Pigs	2 head 3,500
Vegetables and Condiments	1,440
Invitations	150
Wedding Gown Rental	650
Flowers	(300)
Rental Equipment	1,800
Pictures (groom paid)	(500)
Room Decoration	3,000
Liquor	2,400
Musicians (groom paid)	(500)
Gifts to Mother-in-law	200
Cigarettes	360
Other Gifts	520
Shoes	150
Gold Bracelet	1,270
Miscellaneous	–
Total	17,800
Bride Price	30,000
From Groom's Party	5,000
From Other Guests	8,000
Other Gifts	750
Calculated Net	– 3,050
Stated Net	– 4,000

28. According to the information on the chart, the family hosting the ceremony
   (1) was rich
   (2) went bankrupt because of the wedding
   (3) ended up with a deficit
   (4) made a profit on gifts
   (5) relied totally on borrowed money

29. About which of the following cultural concerns could an anthropologist learn from this chart?
   (1) the Thai kinship structure
   (2) bridal folklore
   (3) the nature of the ritual
   (4) Thai wedding customs
   (5) the importance of hospitality to the Thai

30. In what major way is a Thai wedding different from an American wedding?
   (1) provision of entertainment
   (2) the giving of gifts
   (3) the sending of invitations
   (4) the payment of a bride price
   (5) the provision of food

Items 31–33 refer to the following passage.

In the 1970's, the study of peasants was integrated into the mainstream of anthropological research because of a renewed interest in the idea of acculturation. Acculturation is the adoption by one culture of a more dominant culture's way of life. Within the new model of the transformation of society, the peasant was supposed to fall between the tribal culture and the town culture. One group of anthropologists defined the peasants as the folk, as opposed to hunters-gatherers and city dwellers. Another group associated peasants with pre-industrial cities as a contrast to an elite economy. Yet another group saw the peasants as the exploited people who produced a surplus which was siphoned off by the elite class.

31. Apparently, anthropologists are having trouble

    (1) finding any peasants to study
    (2) agreeing on who the elite classes are
    (3) defining who the peasants are
    (4) recognizing the process of acculturation
    (5) separating the elite class from the peasant class

32. The passage supports the conclusion that a major tool used in the study of culture is

    (1) the political structure of a society
    (2) the economic factor
    (3) the folklore of a group
    (4) religious affiliation
    (5) community size

33. Anthropologists are concerned with setting up a new cultural model because

    (1) all the primitive cultures are gone
    (2) there is a large peasant class in the United States
    (3) they realize that cultural studies should not be limited to non-Western primitive peoples
    (4) the peasant class is a new category that had to be accounted for
    (5) the elite classes want to be studied also

34. For years, anthropologists have called folklorists "butterfly collectors" because folklorists have gathered information on things such as riddles, jokes, tales, dance, song, clothing, and housing patterns. The best defense of the folklorist is most likely that

    (1) butterflies should be collected because they are beautiful
    (2) these details are reflections of major cultural patterns and beliefs
    (3) the cultural studies of folklorists are of no concern to anthropologists
    (4) these things are more important than looking at overall cultural patterns
    (5) the study of folklore is as old as anthropology and so should be respected

Answers begin on page 105.

Social Studies Test A

Directions

What Kind of Questions? The Social Studies Test consists of multiple-choice questions intended to measure general social studies concepts. The questions are based on short readings which often include a graph, map, chart, or diagram. Study the information given and then answer the question(s) that follow it. Refer to the information as often as necessary in answering the questions.

How Long Is It? The test is timed. You should spend no more than 85 minutes answering the questions on this test. Work carefully, but do not spend too much time on any one question. Be sure you answer every question. Incorrect answers will not count against you.

How To Mark Answers: Record your answers to the questions on the separate answer sheet provided on page 109. To record each of your answers, mark the numbered space on the answer sheet beside the number that corresponds to the question on the test. The following example has been done for you.

EXAMPLE

Early pioneers of the western frontier looked to settle on land that had adequate access to game and fowl. For this reason, many early pioneers settled on land near

(1) rivers
(2) grasslands
(3) forests
(4) glaciers
(5) oceans

① ② ④ ⑤

The correct answer is <u>forests</u>; therefore, answer space 3 should be marked on the answer sheet.

Do not make any stray or unnecessary marks on the answer sheet. If you change an answer, erase your first mark completely. Mark only one answer space for each question. Multiple answers will be scored as incorrect.

You may now begin Test A.

Directions: Choose the one best answer for each item below.

Items 1–6 refer to the following map.

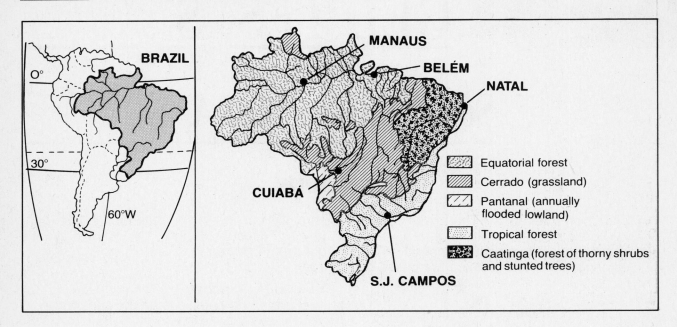

1. The map can be used to discover

   (1) the major agricultural products of Brazil
   (2) Brazil's population densities
   (3) the location of mountains and plateaus
   (4) the location of mineral resources
   (5) major patterns of vegetation

2. According to the map, the least desirable area of Brazil is

   (1) the Equator
   (2) Natal
   (3) Manaus
   (4) approximately 15° S, 60° W
   (5) approximately 30° S, 70° W

3. Which of the following would best describe the climate of Brazil's equatorial forest?

   (1) cold and rainy
   (2) cold and snowy
   (3) mild and dry
   (4) mild and wet
   (5) hot and wet

4. According to the map, Brazil is

   (1) the smallest South American country
   (2) the largest South American country
   (3) the largest Asian country
   (4) the smallest Asian country
   (5) a large island off the coast of South America

5. Details of the map support the conclusion that

   (1) Brazil is not a highly developed country
   (2) Brazil has few natural resources
   (3) Brazil's natural resources have not been fully exploited
   (4) there are only five major cities in Brazil
   (5) Brazil is larger than the United States

6. The best area for raising herd animals is most likely

   (1) the equatorial forest
   (2) the cerrado
   (3) the pantanal
   (4) the tropical forest
   (5) the caatinga

Item 7 refers to the following cartoon.

"LET'S NOT WORK SO HARD GROWING OUR OWN SAFE-TO-EAT VEGETABLES THAT WE BREATHE TOO MUCH OF THIS AIR."

7. The cartoon supports the conclusion that

(1) home gardens are not really worth the effort
(2) growing one's own safe-to-eat vegetables helps the overall environment
(3) individual efforts to combat environmental problems are threatened by even larger environmental ills
(4) growing safe-to-eat vegetables is more difficult than growing regular vegetables
(5) gardening is good exercise

8. The earth has seven major landmasses known as continents. The continents are Africa, Antarctica, Asia, Australia, North America, South America, and Europe. What makes Australia different from the other continents is that it

(1) is in the southern hemisphere
(2) was settled by the English
(3) had a native population when it was discovered
(4) has no actual inhabitants
(5) is the only one that is also a country

9. Although some geographical boundaries are created by natural formations such as rivers and mountains, others are artificially created by people, such as the borders between nations, states, and countries. While forces of nature can change natural boundaries, which of the following events would be most likely to affect a political boundary?

(1) an earthquake
(2) a treaty following a war
(3) a trade agreement between nations
(4) the building of an international railroad
(5) an internal overthrow of a country's government

Items 10–15 refer to the following passage.

In 1619, twenty Africans were brought to Virginia by a Dutch trading ship and exchanged for supplies. They were accepted as indentured servants to be freed from servitude after a specified time. But because they were so different in speech and appearance from the English settlers, these men and women were viewed only as a source of needed labor and were not freed after the time of indenture was over. By 1776, even such distinguished patriots as Washington and Jefferson ran their estates by using slave labor. However, despite his dependence on and recognition of the economic advantages of slavery, Jefferson was intellectually opposed to the institution and made arrangements to eventually free his own slaves.

10. The inference that can be made from the passage is that

   (1) the beginning of slavery in America was planned in advance
   (2) the status of the English indentured servant was easily violated
   (3) the twenty Africans were more than willing to work cheaply
   (4) slavery was well established by the time of the American Revolution
   (5) Washington was morally unfit to be president

11. Even though Jefferson may have had his slaves in mind when he wrote that all men are created equal, this principle was not generally thought of as applying to the black slaves because

   (1) Washington disagreed with him
   (2) they had been regarded for too long as property rather than people
   (3) most slaves were women
   (4) Jefferson had not yet freed his slaves
   (5) slavery existed only in Virginia

12. The attitudes of the Virginia colonials bear a resemblance to those which allowed

   (1) the German people to ignore the actions of Adolf Hitler
   (2) hippies to be arrested for protesting against the war
   (3) laws against child labor
   (4) women's suffrage movements to continue for so long without result
   (5) the prohibition of alcohol

13. According to the passage, the first president of the United States was

   (1) against the institution of slavery
   (2) a slave holder
   (3) a hard man to work for
   (4) planning to free the slaves
   (5) in favor of indentured servants

14. The passage implies that a primary reason for the adoption of slavery in the United States was that

   (1) the Virginia settlers were immoral
   (2) the slave traders were very persuasive
   (3) slavery had been a tradition in England
   (4) there was a serious shortage of workers in colonial America
   (5) the president of the United States approved

15. The best title for this passage is

   (1) The Hardest Choice
   (2) Colonial Cleverness
   (3) A Fateful Trade
   (4) How History Repeats Itself
   (5) Why Jefferson Became President

Item 16 refers to the following graph.

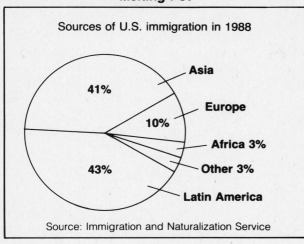

Melting Pot

Sources of U.S. immigration in 1988

- Asia 41%
- Europe 10%
- Africa 3%
- Other 3%
- Latin America 43%

Source: Immigration and Naturalization Service

16. The percentage of immigrants from Asia and Latin America is best explained by

(1) the excellent employment opportunities in those areas of the world
(2) the cultural similarities between Asian and Latin American countries
(3) a lack of available jobs in their own countries
(4) an American prejudice against European immigrants
(5) a growing need for unskilled labor in the United States

Item 17 refers to the following cartoon.

"CONFIDENTIALLY, DON'T YOU JUST *HATE IT* WHEN THE WORKERS OF THE WORLD UNITE?"

17. The cartoon supports the conclusion that

(1) world leaders are in favor of strikes
(2) Communist world leaders are losing faith in their systems
(3) Communist world leaders are confident they can control workers' strikes
(4) workers' strikes are causing trouble for leaders of Communist countries
(5) strikes cannot solve the workers' problems

Item 18 refers to the following cartoon.

The Working "People."

18. According to this turn-of-the-century cartoon,

(1) working people were pleased with their jobs
(2) people will usually follow a strong leader
(3) some individuals profited at the expense of other people's labor
(4) unions were the result of workers' dissatisfaction
(5) the construction industry was more profitable then than now

19. One hundred years after the Emancipation Proclamation, the issue of civil rights was brought again to the nation's attention. Dr. Martin Luther King, Jr. advocated nonviolent demonstrations to protest against racial discrimination. The increase in black voter registration in southern states from an average of 5% to 37% in 1956 to an average of 11% to 69% in 1964 is an example of

(1) an increase in the black population
(2) racial discrimination
(3) violation of civil rights
(4) nonviolent assertion of civil rights
(5) a protest demonstration

Items 20–25 refer to the following passage.

Premier Khrushchev's Condolences: And in Moscow, Premier Nikita Khrushchev went to the U.S. Embassy with Foreign Minister Andrei Gromyko. Khrushchev joined Ambassador Foy Kohler upstairs at Spasso House and spent nineteen minutes with him. Gromyko, observers said, was weeping as they left.

Not long afterward, a pretty, red-haired girl in a flower-print babushka brought in a pot of flowers. Identifying herself as Tatiana Babrashnaya, a typist, she said, tears on her face, "No, I don't have anything to do with America. I brought it because I liked your President."

In a manner impossible to the chancelleries and the palaces—however heartfelt their words of sympathy—Tatiana had expressed the anguish and sorrow of ordinary millions in the U.S., South America, Africa, Asia, and Europe. Simple people everywhere felt the loss almost as a death in the family. In different places, they reacted differently— each in his own way. In Wall Street, the reaction was panic; nervous sellers forced the Dow Jones industrial average down 21.16 points before the exchange was ordered closed. In West Fresno, Calif., Bernard Ybarra, 50, a Mexican-American, and J.H. Williams, 19, a Negro, were looking for farm jobs in the State Labor Office when the radio broke in.

"President Kennedy is dead," the radio announcer said.

Ybarra cried softly. "It ain't true. It ain't true."

Williams, leaving to buy a bottle of wine, said, "What's going to come of us now that a Southerner is President?"

20. The main idea of the passage is that

(1) officials in the Soviet Union mourned John Kennedy's death
(2) people from all walks of life felt the impact of the president's assassination
(3) Kennedy was regarded as one of the most influential presidents of the twentieth century
(4) the political situation in the United States fell apart when Kennedy died
(5) the first reaction to Kennedy's assassination was one of anger

21. The incident involving Tatiana Babrashnaya supports the opinion that

(1) secretaries always provide the right touch
(2) ordinary people are more sincere than politicians
(3) not all Soviet citizens are hardhearted
(4) many people admired Kennedy because of the kind of person he was and not just because he was a political figure
(5) nationality has little to do with political preferences

22. The Dow Jones industrial average went down because

(1) brokers were too depressed to buy
(2) sellers believed Kennedy's death would affect the economy
(3) the stock exchange closed early that day
(4) it was feared that the Communists would attack the United States
(5) brokers feared a return to mass unemployment

23. H.J. Williams's worried question is best explained by

(1) his fear that a southerner would ignore the unemployed
(2) his distress that the man he had voted for was dead
(3) his concern that the civil rights movement would be hurt
(4) a personal distrust of Lyndon Johnson
(5) his sympathy for Ybarra's distress

24. The best title for the passage is

(1) The Shot Felt Around the World
(2) A Nation's Sorrow
(3) The Fate of a President
(4) Death Claims Us All
(5) A Man of the People

25. The passage supports the conclusion that political leaders

(1) come to respect each other even if they are enemies
(2) know how to appear sympathetic
(3) value the opinion of the common people
(4) cannot express sympathy well
(5) realize their own shaky positions

Items 26–31 refer to the following passage.

As barter is no longer a practical way for most people to get the items needed for modern living, many societies use some form of money as their major medium of exchange. The dollar is the basis for currency in the United States and is recognized in two forms, coins and paper. Because the dollar is accepted as a standard and has a value guaranteed by the federal government, dollar payments are accepted for both products and services. Because the government has declared paper money to represent an actual commodity (the gold reserve), paper money along with coins is called legal tender.

26. Which of the following can also be called legal tender?

(1) a handwritten IOU
(2) a verbal promise to repay a debt
(3) a check written on an approved bank form
(4) a receipt
(5) a bank statement

27. Which of the following reasons best explains why barter has become impractical?

(1) People no longer have the time to argue over the worth of an item.
(2) Our society has become too complex to trade on an item-per-item basis.
(3) People are easily cheated when they use the barter system.
(4) Marketplaces have vanished from most cities.
(5) Barter requires skills that we no longer have.

28. An exchange system that uses paper money can work only when

(1) the paper is of high quality
(2) the paper can be recycled to produce new bills
(3) barter systems do not work
(4) the people trust the government reserve system
(5) it includes lower denominations in coins

29. Which of the following best explains the use of coins in a monetary system based on the dollar?

(1) Coins are easier to carry around.
(2) Coins are necessary for use in vending machines.
(3) Sales taxes on small items can be paid with coins.
(4) Silver and copper are very plentiful metals.
(5) The dollar can be divided into smaller denominations.

30. According to the passage, the dollars we use today are

(1) valueless
(2) valuable in their own right
(3) representing the gold held by the Federal Reserve System
(4) worth more than the current exchange rate
(5) representing goods that might otherwise be bartered

31. An international bank would not exchange dollars for which of the following?

(1) Russian rubles
(2) Japanese yen
(3) German marks
(4) Canadian furs
(5) Mexican pesos

Items 32–37 refer to the following chart.

Sources of Personal Income in the United States, 1982

Sources of Personal Income (Functional Distribution)

Type of Income	Amount of Income (billions of $)	Percent of Total Personal Income
Wages, salaries, and other labor income less contributions for social insurance	$1,612.7	62.5%
Personal rental income	49.9	1.9
Personal interest income	366.2	14.2
Personal dividend income	66.4	2.6
Net income of unincorporated businesses (including farms)	108.9	4.2
Transfer payments	374.5	14.5
Total	**$2,578.6**	**100.0%**

32. The inference that can be made from the chart is that

(1) rental property is a sound investment
(2) only a small percent of Americans are private farm owners
(3) most Americans have large savings accounts
(4) social security contributions are 14.5% of a person's gross income
(5) many Americans own small businesses

33. Which of the following can be learned from the chart?

(1) average personal income in the United States
(2) how many people have personal dividend income
(3) if people have income from more than one source
(4) total personal income in the United States
(5) average family income in the United States

34. If transfer payments include unemployment compensation, social security benefits, and public welfare assistance, then as much as 14% of total personal income

    (1) is not related to work
    (2) comes from the government
    (3) is undeserved
    (4) goes to the elderly
    (5) is not taxable

35. The division of income into categories such as wages and rental income is called

    (1) functional distribution of income
    (2) personal income
    (3) percent of total income
    (4) income analysis
    (5) net income

36. If this chart was compared to similar charts for 1984, 1986, and 1988, the figures could be used to

    (1) improve the nation's economy
    (2) analyze trends in personal income sources
    (3) assess the effects of changes in tax laws
    (4) analyze investment trends
    (5) determine changes in average personal income

37. According to the chart, the smallest source of personal income in 1982 was

    (1) interest income
    (2) dividend income
    (3) rental income
    (4) transfer payments
    (5) income of unincorporated businesses

Item 38 refers to the following graph.

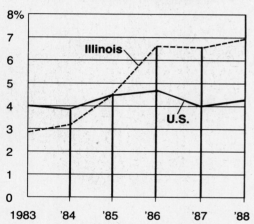

S & L Capital Ratios
Net worth as a percent of assets

Source: Sheshunoff Information Services, Inc.

38. According to the graph, which of the following opinions about savings and loan institutions is justified?

    (1) Good intentions on the part of a savings and loan institution can offset bad debts.
    (2) Not all institutions can be judged accurately by the national average.
    (3) Savings and loan institutions are weaker than regular banks.
    (4) These institutions have grown steadily weaker over the years.
    (5) People will put money into any institution if the reward is great enough.

39. In 1949, the United States had refused to recognize the official existence of the People's Republic of China. When President Nixon made the first trip to China in 1972, he made

    (1) a serious political mistake
    (2) friends with Zhou Enlai
    (3) a step toward ending the cold war with a major power
    (4) a step toward introducing communism to the United States
    (5) peace with Taiwan

40. The Watergate scandal of the early 1970's revealed that even the president could be involved in unethical campaign strategies. When President Nixon resigned in 1974, he was reacting to the high value Americans place on

(1) the integrity of the office of president
(2) political loyalty
(3) personal honesty
(4) the judicial system
(5) national security

41. In 1981, a professor announced to her class that the 52 American hostages in Iran had been released after 444 days in captivity. Her students had no idea what she was talking about. In despair, she assigned students to read news articles and watch television newscasts in addition to the usual homework. The teacher was upset that her students placed so little value on

(1) doing their studies
(2) the right to freedom
(3) international politics
(4) television as a source of news
(5) American lives

Item 42 refers to the following cartoon.

By David Seavey, USA TODAY

Copyright 1989, USA TODAY. Reprinted with permission.

42. The main idea of the cartoon is that

(1) many criminals are back on the streets because the prisons cannot hold all those convicted
(2) rehabilitation programs in prisons are not effective
(3) prison rehabilitation programs are working so well that many convicts are getting out on parole
(4) too many innocent people are being sentenced to jail terms
(5) prison conditions are so bad that inmates are rioting in the streets

Items 43–48 refer to the following passage.

A majority of the American people appear to be politically apathetic; that is, they don't know much or care about the details of the political process. People care more about their personal lives than the more distant and abstract issues of politics. Only when the affairs of government intrude on citizens' private lives or smack of juicy scandal do people pay attention. A prime indicator of such apathy is voter turnout. In the congressional elections of 1974 and 1978, only one-third of eligible voters went to the polls, and only a little over half voted in the 1984 presidential election.

43. General political apathy explains why the media concentrates on

    (1) the private lives of political candidates
    (2) the major issues during campaign years
    (3) international rather than national politics
    (4) statistical analysis of political performance
    (5) actively praising politicians

44. Which of the following would most likely cause people to pay attention to political events?

    (1) a good ad campaign
    (2) the development of a third political party
    (3) a presidential election
    (4) the threat of a repression
    (5) the threat of war

45. If most people know little about politics, which of the following reasons would they most likely give for supporting a particular political party?

    (1) because that party was supported by the person's parents
    (2) because they flipped a coin to make the choice
    (3) because they paid attention to the issues
    (4) because they are protesting being called the silent majority
    (5) because they wish to make a political statement

46. Which of the following statements does not suggest political apathy?

    (1) Politicians just talk a lot.
    (2) I never got around to registering to vote.
    (3) Last year I signed a petition protesting that bill.
    (4) I don't really know enough to make a choice.
    (5) Politics is just a waste of time.

47. Which of the following reasons is least likely to be given by a person who fails to vote on an issue?

    (1) Everyone is happy with the way things are.
    (2) Politicians cannot be trusted.
    (3) Voting doesn't change things.
    (4) Politicians don't care about the people.
    (5) Government is run only for a few special interests.

48. Evidence from the passage supports the conclusion that the presidency was won in 1984 by

    (1) a vote of three-fourths of the eligible voters
    (2) a vote of less than half the eligible voters
    (3) a two-thirds majority of all eligible voters
    (4) Ronald Reagan
    (5) a surprisingly large voter turnout

49. The United Nations is an international organization designed to maintain international peace and to encourage cultural and economic exchange between nations. The existence of such an organization assumes that member nations

(1) are in agreement on all vital issues
(2) are culturally similar
(3) will try to work out their political differences
(4) expect another world war
(5) have economic resources that they are willing to share

50. In a totalitarian government, the leaders recognize no one else's authority and use the government to control almost all aspects of civilian life. There is only one political party, and policies are often imposed by force. In a totalitarian government, there would be no

(1) governmental control of the mass media
(2) centralized armed forces
(3) room for Communist theory
(4) free elections
(5) political dissidents

51. A percentage of campaign funds for congressional candidates comes from political action committees (PACs) which represent special interest groups. In 1988, over 4,000 PACs had contributed about $100 million to political campaigns. There are many PACs because

(1) there are many special interests
(2) elected officials that PACs support in turn support the special interests
(3) members of Congress only want their money
(4) they represent the democratic interests of many people
(5) most of their negotiations are done in secret

Items 52–57 refer to the following definitions.

in-group—the group to which a person belongs
out-group—the group to which a person does not belong
primary group—a small, individual-oriented group with feelings of closeness; a very personal and informal group
secondary group—a goal-oriented group that is fairly impersonal and formal
social category—people who share a characteristic but do not think of themselves as a group

52. Which of the following is the best example of a primary group?

(1) the National Rifle Association
(2) the United States Army
(3) a doctor and her patients
(4) an Alcoholics Anonymous group
(5) the student body of a small college

53. A fourteen-year-old boy who is a member of a street gang in a large city would most likely consider the local YMCA to be

(1) his in-group
(2) an out-group
(3) his primary group
(4) an important secondary group
(5) an important social category

66

54. The definitions help to identify

   (1) the members of different social groups
   (2) the basic characteristics of social groups
   (3) the importance of social groups
   (4) the nature of group behavior
   (5) the reasons people want to belong to a group

55. A sociologist studying in-groups and out-groups would be least interested in

   (1) an individual member's viewpoint
   (2) why certain people are accepted or rejected by different groups
   (3) what characteristics are shared by group members
   (4) what group members do when they are together
   (5) very self-reliant people

56. People in a social category might become a secondary group because

   (1) they discover they have a common interest
   (2) they want to be popular
   (3) social behavior depends on group interaction
   (4) they have nothing in common
   (5) no primary group is appealing

57. Sociologists can best be described as

   (1) members of a social category
   (2) overly curious about personal information
   (3) members of an in-group
   (4) more interested in terminology than in people
   (5) interested primarily in individual behavior

---

58. The famous actor Sir Laurence Olivier suffered from stage fright all his life. He sometimes became so nervous that he asked another actor to stand in the wings off-stage to reassure him. If Olivier had consulted a psychologist, he would most likely have talked about

   (1) insomnia
   (2) anxiety
   (3) depression
   (4) fear of heights
   (5) indecision

59. Anthropologist Arnold van Gennep called the ceremonies that celebrate the transitional stages in life "rites of passage." These ceremonies mark important changes and events such as birth, marriage, and death. Which of the following events is an American rite of passage?

   (1) a college reunion
   (2) a Halloween party
   (3) a Fourth of July celebration
   (4) a high school graduation
   (5) an office Christmas party

60. Psychologists have found that mothers may unknowingly reinforce sexual stereotypes in the way they talk to their children. Mothers tend to ask more mathematical questions of their sons and to use numbers less when talking to their daughters. These findings support the conclusion that

   (1) girls are not as curious as boys
   (2) boys are thought to be better at math than girls
   (3) most mothers don't know what they're talking about
   (4) boys are better at giving answers than girls
   (5) girls are thought to be better mathematicians than boys

61. One researcher has suggested that people think that talking about how good one feels or how well one is doing can sound too much like self-praise. This may explain why

   (1) most people are unhappy
   (2) people talk more about their troubles
   (3) happy people are unpopular
   (4) people develop low self-images
   (5) self-confident people don't have much to say

62. When early anthropologists came across unfamiliar behaviors in the people they studied, they often attributed what they didn't understand to native irrationality. This mistake was corrected when anthropologist Bronislaw Malinowski pointed out that native cultures, however unfamiliar, had their own well-developed rules of social behavior. Malinowski realized that

(1) he sometimes acted irrationally himself
(2) culture itself is not rational
(3) being different does not mean being illogical
(4) the natives were willing to explain why they did everything
(5) he was more intelligent than the other anthropologists

63. To the Ibo of Nigeria, to "get up" means to promote the welfare of one's village. A developing town is a source of pride to its residents, and a good citizen is one who helps the town "get up." Ibo youths who return to their villages after earning money in the city show that they value

(1) "getting themselves up"
(2) city life
(3) their home communities
(4) their own prestige
(5) a simple life

Item 64 refers to the following diagram.

Lineage of a Ulithi Man   (See man in dark triangle)

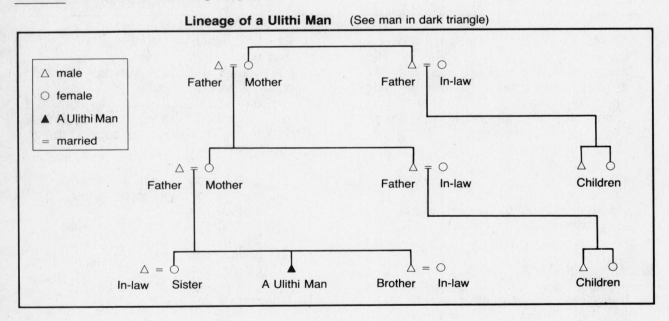

64. The Ulithi of Micronesia classify most of their relatives as either mother and father, brother and sister, in-laws, or children. A man's nephews and nieces are called his children, and his uncle is called his father. According to the diagram, a Ulithi man would call

(1) his sister's husband "brother"
(2) his brother's wife "sister"
(3) his brother's wife "mother"
(4) his mother's father "brother"
(5) his sister's husband "in-law"

GED Social Studies Test A

Answers and Explanations

1. **(5)** (Comprehension) The only information given is for the major patterns of vegetation. There is no reference on the map for any of the other options.

2. **(4)** (Analysis) The least attractive area according to the map is the pantanal which floods yearly. Options (2) and (3) are not only cities, but they appear to be in favorable locations. The Equator, Option (1), runs through the rain forest and is probably more enjoyable than the pantanal. Option (5) is the location of S.J. Campos in the tropical forest. Both maps must be used to determine the location of the pantanal.

3. **(5)** (Evaluation) The Equator is one of the warmer regions of the earth. The forest would most likely be hot and would, therefore, eliminate the other options.

4. **(2)** (Comprehension) The map clearly shows that Brazil is the largest country in South America. The other options are not true.

5. **(3)** (Evaluation) The large forests constitute a major resource; if they had been fully exploited, they would not figure so prominently on the map. Therefore, Option (2) is wrong. The map does not provide sufficient information to determine Options (1), (4), or (5).

6. **(2)** (Application) The cerrado is grassland and would best support herd animals. The other options would not support herd animals.

7. **(3)** (Evaluation) The small effort to have chemical-free food is in danger because the air itself is toxic. Option (1) is wrong because the garden itself is not the problem. Option (2) is not suggested. There is no evidence for Options (4) and (5).

8. **(5)** (Application) Except for Antarctica, which has no countries, all the other continents are divided into the smaller units of countries.

9. **(2)** (Analysis) Countries often cede or gain territory in the negotiations following a war. The natural event in Option (1) would have no effect on a political division. Options (3) and (4) are wrong because they concern crossing, not changing, a boundary. Option (5) involves events within a boundary.

10. **(4)** (Analysis) Slavery in America began when the Virginia colony Africans were denied their freedom more than 150 years before the American Revolution. There is no support in the passage for Options (1), (2), and (5). Option (3) may have been true, but there is no evidence in the passage about why the Africans were indentured servants to begin with.

11. **(2)** (Analysis) Slaves had to be regarded as human beings in order to be thought of as equal. There is no evidence for Option (1) in the passage. Option (5) is unlikely. Options (3) and (4) would have had no effect on popular opinion.

12. **(1)** (Application) The basic attitude is that someone who is sufficiently different can be treated less than human. This viewpoint allows people to overlook various types of cruelty, even if they do not participate in the act itself. Options (2) and (4) are wrong because they are both more political and less basic to human rights. Option (3) is wrong because it reflects an opposing attitude. Option (5) is wrong because it does not deal with basic human rights.

13. **(2)** (Comprehension) This option is indicated in the passage. None of the other options are supported by the passage.

14. **(4)** (Analysis) The colonists saw the Africans as a new source of cheap labor which was necessary to develop their settlement. Option (1) is wrong because this new group was viewed only as property, so morality didn't apply. As the decision not to free the slaves was made after the Dutch ship had gone, Option (2) is wrong. There is no evidence for Option (3) in the passage, and Option (5) is impossible as there was no president in 1619.

15. **(3)** (Application) As no initial intention was involved, Option (3) best states the impact a single event can have. Because Options (1) and (2) suggest intention, they are wrong. There is no support in the passage for Options (4) and (5).

16. **(3)** (Analysis) Most immigration is motivated by a search for a better economic life. Because of this, Option (1) is unlikely. Options (2) and (5) are not true. There is no basis in the graph for Option (4).

17. **(4)** (Evaluation) The caption supports the conclusion in Option (4) by suggesting a dislike of the situation by the world leaders; this eliminates Option (1). Option (3) is wrong because there is no suggestion in the cartoon of plans to control strikes. There is no evidence in the cartoon for Options (2) and (5).

18. **(3)** (Comprehension) There is a clear difference between the well-dressed man and the workers. That he is in the lead suggests that he has control over them and uses them to make money. The facial expressions of the workers indicate that Option (1) is wrong. Although Options (2) and (4) may be true statements, they are not referred to in the cartoon. There is no evidence in the cartoon for Option (5).

19. **(4)** (Application) Voter registration is an important civil right and does not involve violence. Option (1) is wrong because population figures have nothing to do with who registers. Options (2) and (3) have no support in the information. Option (5) is wrong because voter registration is not a demonstration even if it can later be used as a tool of protest.

20. **(2)** (Comprehension) There were several examples of people who mourned Kennedy's death. Option (1) is wrong because it is a supporting detail and not the main idea. There is no evidence in the passage to support Options (3), (4), or (5).

21. **(4)** (Evaluation) The gesture was based on personality and not politics. Option (1) suggests it was a calculated gesture and not a gesture from the heart. Options (2) and (3) are wrong because they draw contrasts that are not supported in the passage. There is no support in the passage for Option (5).

22. **(2)** (Analysis) A change in the political scene can have a negative effect on the economy. Option (1) is wrong because the passage refers to nervous sellers. Option (3) is wrong because the market closed after the average went down. Options (4) and (5) have no support in the passage.

23. **(3)** (Analysis) Williams would believe a southern president might be against civil rights and not employment as in Option (1). Option (2) is wrong because Williams was too young to have voted for Kennedy. Options (4) and (5) have no support in the passage.

24. **(1)** (Application) The worldwide shock was the result of a gunshot. Option (2) is wrong because more than one nation was affected. Options (3), (4), and (5) are too general to summarize the passage.

25. **(1)** (Evaluation) The tears of the Soviet leaders indicate respect for Kennedy. Option (2) is wrong because the sorrow was apparently genuine. There is no support in the passage for Options (3), (4), and (5).

26. **(3)** (Application) A check written on a bank is the only equivalent of cash listed. Options (1) and (2) are wrong because they are not backed by the government. Options (4) and (5) are simply records of financial transactions.

27. **(2)** (Analysis) Too many items would have to be traded back and forth to get all the goods and services necessary for life today. Options (1), (4), and (5) may be true, but they are the results and not the cause of the abandonment of barter. There is no evidence for Option (3) in the passage. People can be cheated in any system of exchange.

28. **(4)** (Evaluation) Because paper money is guaranteed by the government, the people must trust the government to provide the equivalent value by using the gold reserve if it had to. But at the same time, the people do not require that payment from the government. Options (1), (2), and (5) are not essential for a money system to work well. Option (3) suggests a false cause and effect.

29. **(5)** Analysis) Option (5) explains the function of coins. Option (1) is not true because coins are heavier than paper. Option (2) is not true because vending machines use coins because coins already existed. Option (3) may be true, but it is not an explanation of the use of coins. Option (4) is wrong because the metals are not plentiful, and this option refers only to material, not value.

30. **(3)** (Comprehension) This is stated in the passage. Neither Option (1) nor Option (2) is true. Options (4) and (5) are not suggested in the passage.

31. **(4)** (Application) A bank would not exchange money for goods. Options (1), (2), (3), and (5) are official forms of currency.

32. **(2)** (Analysis) Private farms are included in the small 4.2% of total income. Option (1) is wrong because there is no evidence in the chart of actual return from rentals. Option (3) is wrong because interest income could be coming from only a small percent of the population. Option (4) is wrong because there is no analysis of gross income on the chart. Option (5) has no support in the chart.

33. **(4)** (Comprehension) This chart provides actual figures for Option (4). The other options cannot be learned from the chart.

34. **(2)** (Application) These payments are all from government programs. Option (1) is wrong because some programs, such as unemployment and social security, are work related. There is no support in the chart for Options (3), (4), or (5).

35. **(1)** (Comprehension) This can be determined from the chart heading. The other options are not supported in the chart.

36. **(2)** (Application) The charts would show changes and developments in sources alone, eliminating Options (3), (4), and (5). Option (1) is wrong because there is no cause and effect relationship between analysis and action.

37. **(3)** (Comprehension) The smallest percent is for rental income. All the other options are higher.

38. **(2)** (Evaluation) The state institution shows a different economic strength than that suggested by the national figure. The other options have no support in the graph.

39. **(3)** (Analysis) The gesture is a step toward ending the conflict between the two countries. It is not a mistake as stated in Option (1). There is no support for Options (2) and (4). The United States had no quarrel with Taiwan as suggested by Option (5).

40. **(1)** (Evaluation) The office of president is a symbol of the strength and honesty of the American people, and so it must be free of scandal. Options (2) and (5) had nothing to do with the scandal. Option (3) is wrong because Americans were less concerned with Nixon as a person than as their representative. Option (4) has no support.

41. **(3)** (Evaluation) The students were not aware of a major political situation. Although the other options may be true, there is no evidence of them in this passage.

42. **(1)** (Comprehension) The word *overflow* suggests that there is no room in the prison for all the prisoners assigned to it. Options (2) and (3) are wrong because there is no evidence in the cartoon of rehabilitation programs. There is no support in the cartoon for Options (4) and (5).

43. **(1)** (Application) Personal scandals involving politicians appeal to the public, so the media covers them. All the other options would appeal to a politically uninterested audience.

44. **(5)** (Application) War would directly affect people's lives. The evidence in the passage is against Options (1), (2), and (3). Option (4) would be a less threatening event than Option (5).

45. **(1)** (Analysis) People often follow tradition when confronted with a choice about which they know very little. Option (2) might be true but probably wouldn't apply to most people. Options (3), (4), and (5) are wrong because they suggest an interest in and knowledge of politics.

46. **(3)** (Application) Signing a petition is a political act. All of the other options do not reflect political apathy.

47. **(1)** (Analysis) It is unlikely that all people are happy with the way things are. The other options are reasons for feeling that an individual's vote is useless.

48. **(2)** (Evaluation) If only a little over half the eligible population voted, Options (1) and (3) are impossible. Option (4) is true but is not documented in the passage. Option (5) is a distortion of fact.

49. **(3)** (Analysis) In order for the United Nations to accomplish its goals, Option (3) would be necessary. Options (1), (2), and (5) are unlikely considering the diversity of the members. There is no support for Option (4).

50. **(4)** (Evaluation) Free elections would undermine a totalitarian government's authority. Option (1) is wrong because media would be controlled. There is insufficient evidence in the text for Options (2), (3), and (5). Option (5) is also wrong because someone would object to total control.

51. **(2)** (Analysis) PACs continue to operate only if their efforts are successful. Options (1), (4), and (5) have nothing to do with the increase of PACs. There is no evidence in the text for Option (3).

52. **(4)** (Application) In such a group, the interaction is necessarily personal. Options (1), (2), and (3) are all goal-oriented, and the people involved are fairly formal with each other. Option (5) may produce primary groups but is not one itself.

53. **(2)** (Application) To a gang member, the socially acceptable YMCA would be unimportant. Options (1), (3), (4), and (5) are incorrect because the gang member most likely would have nothing to do with the YMCA.

54. **(2)** (Comprehension) The definitions describe the nature of a group but not its members. Option (1) is not true. There is no indication in the definitions of Options (3), (4), and (5).

55. **(5)** (Application) Self-reliant people are least likely to be concerned with groups. The other options would provide insight into the nature of in-groups and out-groups.

56. **(1)** (Analysis) The shared characteristic would make members of the social category aware of each other. There is no support for Options (2), (3), and (4). Option (5) is wrong because that eliminates the social category.

57. **(3)** (Application) Sociologists would have much in common with each other and feel a sense of belonging to an academic or intellectually oriented group. Option (1) is incorrect because sociologists would perceive themselves as a group. There is no support for Options (2) and (4). Option (5) is wrong because sociologists are primarily interested in group behavior.

58. **(2)** (Application) Olivier was worried about performance. There is no evidence for Options (1), (3), (4), and (5) in the text.

59. **(4)** (Application) A high school graduation is a symbol of transition from childhood to adulthood. The other options are wrong because they celebrate events not connected to the life cycle.

60. **(2)** (Evaluation) A mother, according to the text, would be sending a signal that boys are better at math than girls. Options (1) and (4) are wrong because they are stated as facts and not opinions. Option (3) is wrong because mothers know what they are saying but perhaps don't understand the implications. Option (5) is not supported in the text.

61. **(2)** (Analysis) Talking about troubles is not considered self-praise. Options (1), (3), (4), and (5) are not supported by the text.

62. **(3)** (Analysis) Malinowski recognized that native peoples acted according to their own well-developed rules of social behavior and that any behavior should not be judged by the standards of another culture. Options (1) and (2) would not support his belief. Option (4) is unlikely. There is no support for Option (5) in the text.

63. **(3)** (Evaluation) To return with money would contribute to the welfare of the village and show they want to "get up." Options (1) and (4) are wrong because the Ibo youths would not return if the options were true. Option (2) is wrong because the Ibo youths left the city. Option (5) is wrong because village life is not necessarily simple.

64. **(5)** (Comprehension) The Ulithi man's sister's husband would be called his in-law. Options (1), (2), and (3) are wrong because these are all spouses and are called in-laws. Option (4) is wrong because his mother's brother would be called his father.

Analysis of Performance on the Simulated GED Social Studies Test A

The chart below will help you determine your strengths and weaknesses in reading comprehension and in the social studies content areas of geography, history, economics, political science, and behavioral science.

Directions

Circle the number of each item that you answered correctly on the Simulated GED Test A. Count the number of items you answered correctly in each column. Write the amount in the total correct space of each column. (For example, if you answered 8 history items correctly, place the number 8 in the blank before out of 16.) Complete this process for the remaining columns.

Count the number of items you answered correctly in each row. Write that amount in the total correct space of each row. (For example, in the comprehension row, write the number correct in the blank before out of 12.) Complete this process for the remaining rows.

Test A   Analysis of Performance Chart

Item Types:	Geography (p. 12–37)	History (p. 38–77)	Economics (p.78–103)	Political Science (p. 104–135)	Behavioral Science (p. 136–153)	Total Correct
Comprehension	①, ④	13, ⑱, 20	30, ㉝, ㉟, ㊲	㊷	54, ㉞	_____ out of 12
Analysis	②, 9	10, 11, 14, ⑯, 22, 23	27, 29, ㉜	39, 45, 47, 49, 51	56, 61, 62	_____ out of 19
Application	⑥, 8	12, 15, 19, 24	26, 31, ㉞, ㊱	43, 44, 46	52, 53, 55, 57, 58, 59	_____ out of 19
Evaluation	③, ⑤, ⑦	⑰, 21, 25	28, ㊳	40, 41, 48, 50	60, 63	_____ out of 14
Total Correct	_____ out of 9	_____ out of 16	_____ out of 13	_____ out of 13	_____ out of 13	Total correct: _____ out of 64 1-50 = Need More Review 51-64 = Congratulations! You're ready!

(Circled items indicate those questions with a graphic stimulus.)

If you answered fewer than 50 of the 64 questions correctly, determine which areas are hardest for you. Go back to the *Steck-Vaughn GED Social Studies* book and review the content in those areas.

In the parentheses under the heading, the page numbers tell you where you can find the beginning of specific instruction about that area of social studies in the *Steck-Vaughn GED Social Studies* book. Also refer to the chart on page 3.

UNIT 2 | SIMULATED GED TESTS

Social Studies Test B

Directions

What Kind of Questions? The Social Studies Test consists of multiple-choice questions intended to measure general social studies concepts. The questions are based on short readings which often include a graph, map, chart, or diagram. Study the information given and then answer the question(s) that follow it. Refer to the information as often as necessary in answering the questions.

How Long Is It? The test is timed. You should spend no more than 85 minutes answering the questions on this test. Work carefully, but do not spend too much time on any one question. Be sure you answer every question. Incorrect answers will not count against you.

How To Mark Answers: Record your answers to the questions on the separate answer sheet provided on page 109. To record each of your answers, mark the numbered space on the answer sheet beside the number that corresponds to the question on the test. The following example has been done for you.

EXAMPLE

Early pioneers of the western frontier looked to settle on land that had adequate access to game and fowl. For this reason, many early pioneers settled on land near

(1) rivers
(2) grasslands
(3) forests
(4) glaciers
(5) oceans   ① ② ❸ ④ ⑤

The correct answer is <u>forests</u>; therefore, answer space 3 should be marked on the answer sheet.

Do not make any stray or unnecessary marks on the answer sheet. If you change an answer, erase your first mark completely. Mark only one answer space for each question. Multiple answers will be scored as incorrect.

You may now begin Test B.

Directions: Choose the <u>one best answer</u> for each item below.

1. Acid rain, which damages plant and animal life, is the result of toxic chemicals combining with water particles in the air. Many Canadians blame the production of the acid rain that is affecting their environment on American industry. This accusation suggests that pollution problems

   (1) can affect relations between friendly nations
   (2) can be solved through a mutual effort
   (3) can be blamed completely on United States factories
   (4) affect Canadians but not Americans
   (5) have nothing to do with Canadian factories

<u>Item 2</u> refers to the following map.

Aquifers in the United States

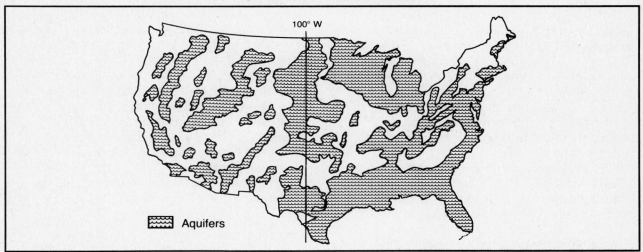

100° W

Aquifers

2. The shaded areas of the map represent aquifers, reservoirs of underground water. The 100°W meridian

   (1) runs across the driest part of the nation
   (2) essentially acts as a boundary between the wet and dry sections of the United States
   (3) runs across an area where there are no aquifers
   (4) follows the course of the Mississippi River
   (5) acts as a division between saltwater and freshwater reservoirs

Item 3 refers to the following map.

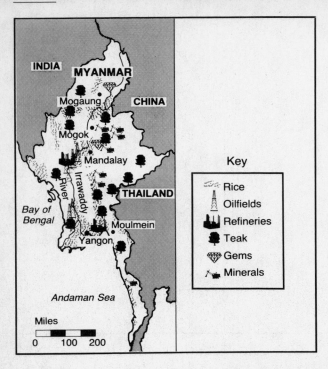

Key
- 〰 Rice
- 🛢 Oilfields
- 🏭 Refineries
- ♣ Teak
- 💎 Gems
- ⚒ Minerals

3. Which of the following cannot be determined from the map?

    (1)   that Myanmar is rich in natural resources
    (2)   that Myanmar is in Asia
    (3)   the distance from Mandalay to Yangon
    (4)   one of Myanmar's food sources
    (5)   the total amount of Myanmar's exports

Items 4–9 refer to the following passage.

Leaning on the black box of a carriage that marked him as a Menonite, Harry Fox told me why he had come to live in that scenic slice of central New York State fondly known as the Finger Lakes.

"This is fine farm country, as good as any in the East. I doubt a man could find pleasanter surroundings for his toil or for raising up a family."

Rachel Malin said much the same thing: "The woods offer their shades, and the fields their harvest...this new world...abounds with almost everything we could wish for."

Both settled on fertile slopes above a misshapen wishbone of water called Keuka Lake. But they will never meet. Harry moved in from Lancaster County, Pennsylvania, in 1975; Rachel migrated from Philadelphia almost two hundred years ago.

The similarity for their views is not surprising. For in this large low-census area, change comes more as a whisper than as the turbulent high wind that has toppled traditional life-styles elsewhere. Even the rush for rural real estate, evident in other places, has done little to disturb the status quo.

Not that anyone I met was seriously anti-progress. It's just that Finger Lakers are a pretty conservative lot, not easily convinced that bigger means better or that new notions always suit their needs.

By nature, they're about as free of sharp edges as the countryside they cherish. The Ice Age created its gentle contours some million years ago. Glaciers, grinding away at a plateau already veined with valleys, mounded some sections into whale-shaped hills called drumlins. Then, gouging debris from former riverbeds, the ice dug deep basins for a chain of dazzling lakes.

4. The population per square mile around the Finger Lakes can best be described as

    (1)   fairly low
    (2)   turbulent
    (3)   quite crowded
    (4)   increasing in a rush
    (5)   higher than average for rural areas

5. The hills and lakes that make up the Finger Lakes area are the result of

    (1)   years of erosion
    (2)   tornado winds
    (3)   glacial action
    (4)   conservation efforts
    (5)   Ice Age storms

6. Harry Fox and Rachel Malin moved to this area of New York because they valued

    (1) peace and quiet
    (2) religious freedom
    (3) the fertile land
    (4) agricultural progress
    (5) freedom from city living

7. Information in the passage supports the opinion that

    (1) even as humans can shape their environment, their environment can shape the nature of humankind
    (2) no land is immune to real estate development
    (3) Pennsylvania is not a good place to live
    (4) people are not affected by where they live
    (5) Finger Lakes will be developed soon

8. The author is not surprised by the similarity in the viewpoints of people born two centuries apart because

    (1) society has not changed all that much
    (2) the land itself has changed little
    (3) America is still the land of the free
    (4) the two shared the same religious view of the land
    (5) Finger Lakes residents are seriously anti-progress

9. Which of the following statements is adequately supported by the passage?

    (1) Conservative people are environmental conservationists.
    (2) Conservative people tend to disturb the status quo.
    (3) Conservative people tend to resist change in their land as well as themselves.
    (4) Conservatives are in favor of rapid progress.
    (5) Conservatives prefer rural areas.

Items 10–15 refer to the following passage.

The Great Depression had an impact on German businesses. German industry, despite all its merits, had a fundamental weakness. It was built on credit. It functioned well as long as Germans could borrow without immediate repayment. Any retraction of promised materials or credit would cause a violent reaction throughout the country's industry. The sudden recall of short-term loans began to endanger the continued operation of numerous plants. Foreign tariffs and quotas had devastating repercussions because most German firms had no reserves on which to draw. When the American stock market crashed in 1929, American agencies began recalling their loans. This had a paralyzing effect on Germany. As the depression deepened, markets were cut off even as demands for repayment increased.

In 1931, the Viennese bank, Kreditanstalt, failed. This prevented German banks from recalling their major deposits with that institution. The widespread bankruptcy and economic confusion which resulted in turn produced massive unemployment.

In 1933, newly-appointed Chancellor Adolf Hitler created employment for 7 million people by ignoring the principles of laissez faire. He sent the unemployed to farms and factories, whether they were needed or not. He drafted the remainder of the unemployed into the military. Within a year and a half, the Nazi government had total control of labor and industry and the German people.

10. German businesses went bankrupt because

    (1) loans they had taken could not be repaid
    (2) the American stock market crashed
    (3) foreign tariffs increased
    (4) materials were no longer available
    (5) they were poorly managed

11. Just as Hitler ignored the principles of competitive business and government noninterference, he later

    (1) ignored principles of human decency
    (2) gave Germany back her dignity
    (3) resisted the appeal of leadership
    (4) paid attention to the demands of labor unions
    (5) ignored the appeal of power

12. The shaky condition of the German economy at the time of the Great Depression is best explained by

    (1) the fairly recent adoption of industrial techniques
    (2) a loss of working capital due to debts incurred during World War I
    (3) the split of Germany into East and West sectors
    (4) the stability of the Viennese bank
    (5) sound investments

13. The information in the passage supports the opinion that

    (1) banks can't be trusted
    (2) buying on credit will lead to disaster
    (3) whoever controls the economy controls the nation
    (4) businesses should not borrow money
    (5) principles of laissez faire are worthless

14. Considering that Hitler ran for the office of chancellor several times, starting in 1930, it can be inferred from the passage that he

    (1) won the election each time
    (2) finally won the election in 1933
    (3) eventually gave up the office
    (4) ran a whirlwind campaign
    (5) never was actually elected

15. The results of the Viennese bank failure can provide some insight into why Americans

    (1) distrust Swiss bank accounts
    (2) were worried by the apparent weakness of savings and loan institutions
    (3) trust only American banks and American currency
    (4) have both savings and checking accounts
    (5) conduct business transactions through lawyers

Items 16–21 refer to the following passage.

The first major coal mine disaster took place in Pennsylvania's Avondale mine on September 6, 1969. A fire in the mine shafts began in the morning and swept through the deep tunnels that were the only available exit for the miners. Not until late that night were rescue attempts begun. This was because no one had turned off the ventilator fan that kept circulating the toxic fumes that resulted from the burning mine. Those hours cost 111 men and boys their lives. The tragedy at first unified the coal workers, who had resisted coalition because of their diverse ethnic backgrounds, into what seemed a solid labor movement. But a rumor was started that the fire had been deliberately set by the Irish Molly Maguires, a secret antimanagement organization. The English and Welsh miners turned against the Irish miners in response, and the miners' moment of unification turned into antagonism and violence of miner against miner.

16. According to the passage, the Avondale mine disaster was caused by

    (1) the Molly Maguires
    (2) a faulty ventilator fan
    (3) a fire of unknown origins
    (4) tension between ethnic groups
    (5) a collapsed tunnel

17. In which of the following American tragedies was the finger of blame also pointed at someone without sufficient cause?

    (1) the great Chicago fire
    (2) San Francisco earthquake
    (3) the assassination of John Kennedy
    (4) the *Challenger* explosion
    (5) the Watergate break-in

18. In their first effort at unification, the miners most likely

(1) demanded better firefighting techniques
(2) protested their health care costs
(3) demanded higher wages
(4) demanded the removal of Irish miners
(5) protested unsafe mine conditions

19. The ease with which the English miners turned against the Irish miners is best explained by

(1) an ingrained dislike of the Welsh
(2) the long-standing antagonism of England and Ireland
(3) the tempers of the English
(4) their drinking habits
(5) threats from the mine owners

20. According to the passage, the Molly Maguires were believed to place little value on

(1) secrecy
(2) the efficiency of violence
(3) the lives of other miners
(4) the need for a miner's union
(5) their Irish heritage

21. If the Molly Maguires existed today, they might be labeled

(1) patriots
(2) union advocates
(3) Communists
(4) socialists
(5) terrorists

22. In the mid 1800's, the American people believed that our country had a manifest destiny, a goal of becoming a world power. Part of the dream was to include all the land to the Pacific Ocean in the United States. Evidence of the reality of manifest destiny came when

(1) a dispute occurred between England and the United States over ownership of the Oregon Territory
(2) President Polk acquired the territories of Oregon, Texas, and California
(3) Henry Clay lost the 1944 presidential election
(4) Texas declared independence from Spain in 1836 and became the Lone Star Republic
(5) Marcus Whitman led a thousand people westward on the Oregon Trail

23. After the Civil War, a Reconstruction government was set up in the South with federal troops sent from the North to keep the peace. Often Southerners were not allowed to hold public office or even to vote. Which of the following slogans would many Southerners have agreed with the most?

(1) We shall not be moved.
(2) Just say no.
(3) Give peace a chance.
(4) No taxation without representation.
(5) Let the good times roll.

24. In 1887, Congress passed the Interstate Commerce Act which regulated the railroads, ensuring that shipping and travel rates were the same for all customers. The best explanation for this legislation is that

(1) the government wanted to control big business
(2) farmers had been charged higher fares than industrial tycoons
(3) taxes on income from the railroads could be better assessed
(4) the railroads had too much competition
(5) people were no longer using the railroads

Item 25 refers to the following chart.

American Newspapers 1860–1900

Year	Number of Daily Newspapers	Total Daily Circulation
1860	387	1,478,000
1870	574	2,602,000
1880	971	3,566,000
1890	1,610	8,387,000
1900	2,226	15,102,000

25. The difference in the figures in 1860 and 1900 of the number of newspapers published was influenced the most by

(1) the founding of the American Library Association in 1876
(2) the increase in public high schools from 160 in 1870 to 6,000 in 1900
(3) a growing public interest in sensationalism
(4) a decrease in college enrollment
(5) the establishment of 15 graduate schools by the year 1900

26. Using a credit card has become a common way of making a purchase in the United States. Convenient as it may be, a credit card is not simply a substitute for ready cash. It is a loan on which interest is paid, usually after the first installment is due. To use a credit card wisely, a consumer should

(1) plan to pay only the monthly minimum charge
(2) budget for the additional finance charges
(3) charge to the available limit
(4) make small payments over a long period of time
(5) never charge anything

Reprinted with special permission of King Features Syndicate, Inc.

27. Which of the following best explains why this cartoon could be used as a promotion for consumer education?

(1) One hundred and fifty dollars is not very much money.
(2) Five years is a long time to wait for a reward.
(3) The proceeds from lotteries pay for state projects.
(4) A small investment can yield worthwhile results.
(5) The amount of money spent is often much less than the amount of the reward.

28. Economic inflation is an overall and often disproportionate rise in the general price level. Inflation of the dollar means that a consumer can buy less with a set amount of money than was possible earlier. When inflation continues to develop, the name for the problem is especially understandable because

(1) the consumer's budget is stretched to its limit
(2) the size of the dollar bill seems to get larger
(3) the bill collector's voice gets louder
(4) the cost of living has gone up
(5) a consumer often has to get a second job to keep up with the bills

Item 29 refers to the following cartoon.

Reprinted by permission of UFS, Inc.

29. The cartoonist is expressing the opinion that

(1) Congress is successfully reducing the federal deficit
(2) congressional representatives are underpaid
(3) Congress has met too many times
(4) a congressional pay raise is inappropriate
(5) a pay raise will not affect the federal budget

Item 30 refers to the following graph.

Construction Spending
In billions of dollars, seasonally adjusted

Source: Commerce Department, Bureau of Labor Statistics

30. The graph supports the opinion that

(1) the construction industry is in decline
(2) few new houses were built in 1987
(3) housing construction boomed in the beginning of 1988
(4) construction trends are unstable
(5) construction spending is fairly predictable

Item 31 refers to the following graph.

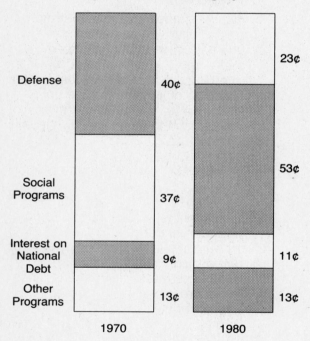

How Much of Each Federal Dollar Was Spent on Each Category

Defense — 40¢ / 23¢
Social Programs — 37¢ / 53¢
Interest on National Debt — 9¢ / 11¢
Other Programs — 13¢ / 13¢

1970 / 1980

31. Which of the following conclusions can be made using the information on this graph?

(1) The national debt increased substantially between 1970 and 1980.
(2) The national debt remained stable over a ten-year period.
(3) National priorities changed between 1970 and 1980.
(4) Americans objected to the amount spent on defense in 1970.
(5) In 1990, less money will be spent on defense than was spent in 1970.

32. The fixed exchange rate is the agreement between nations about what the official trading rate of their currencies will be. National banks can then buy and sell international currency in the world money market. The fixed exchange rate explains

(1) the success of international banking
(2) why an American dollar and a Canadian dollar are often worth different amounts
(3) why rich people put their savings in Swiss bank accounts
(4) the fluctuation of the rate of inflation
(5) why Soviet businesses want to sell goods to the United States

---

Items 33–38 refer to the following passage.

Allison and Gillian are excellent cooks and have degrees in business. They have decided to open a pastry and tea shop in the downtown area of a large city. Between them, they have plenty of capital, enthusiasm, energy, and know-how. They know their enterprise can either succeed or fail. If customers enjoy the food and atmosphere, they will return and recommend it to other people. Then Allison and Gillian can concentrate on improving the shop and developing a larger selection of pastries to attract even more customers. It is also possible that the business will attract few customers and that some may not return. Then the prepared foods will have to be replaced with new pastries, more efforts will have to be spent on trying to attract customers, and eventually Allison and Gillian's initial enthusiasm will be gone. They will be less interested in putting time and money into their business.

33. The best name for Allison and Gillian's economic theory is

(1) How To Succeed in Business Without Really Trying
(2) The Business Spiral
(3) Work Hard and Be Rewarded
(4) What To Do With Old Bread
(5) The Cookie Crumbles

34. The main idea of the passage is that once the initial effort has been invested

(1) a good idea can't fail
(2) the business will run itself
(3) the rest depends on the response of the customer
(4) the owners will lose interest
(5) the money will roll in

35. If Allison and Gillian do not make good pastries, their shop will

(1) become dark and dingy
(2) go out of business
(3) have to move from the downtown area
(4) begin to attract customers
(5) need more capital

36. By going into business, Allison and Gillian are assuming

(1) they will fail, but they have to try anyway
(2) they will succeed because they know how to avoid the problems
(3) they can always turn a failing business around
(4) one doesn't really run a business; it runs you
(5) they have a chance at success

37. The possibilities of being successful or not successful are

    (1) totally unrealistic
    (2) what many new businesses face
    (3) faced only by restaurant owners
    (4) what make downtown areas poor business locations
    (5) major puzzles to economists

38. Information in the passage supports the conclusion that

    (1) women shouldn't own businesses
    (2) a pastry shop is not a risky business
    (3) advertising by word of mouth is expensive
    (4) a restaurant's inventory should be fresh
    (5) variety is the key to success

Items 39–44 refer to the following map.

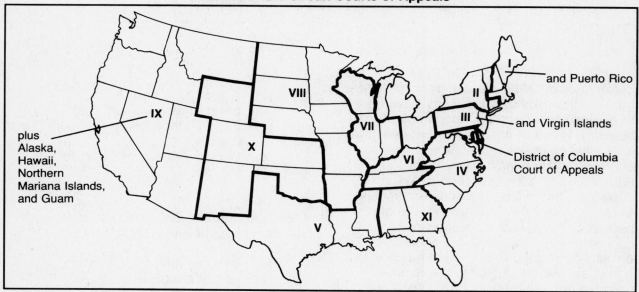

Districts of the Circuit Courts of Appeals

plus Alaska, Hawaii, Northern Mariana Islands, and Guam

and Puerto Rico

and Virgin Islands

District of Columbia Court of Appeals

39. According to the map, a case appealed in California would be heard by

    (1) the Tenth District Circuit Court of Appeals
    (2) the Ninth District Circuit Court of Appeals
    (3) the Second District Circuit Court of Appeals
    (4) the Eighth District Circuit Court of Appeals
    (5) the Eleventh District Court of Appeals

40. There are fewer circuit courts of appeals west of the Mississippi River because

    (1) people settle their differences on their own
    (2) crime is less violent than in the area east of the Mississippi River
    (3) there aren't many judges willing to sit on courts of appeals
    (4) the population density is much lower than in the area east of the Mississippi River
    (5) the courts were established much later than in the area east of the Mississippi River

41. What reason best explains why there is a separate court of appeals that includes only the District of Columbia?

    (1) The president likes to preside over the court of appeals.
    (2) It is a state.
    (3) There is a very high local rate of court appeals.
    (4) Members of Congress need a place to take their constituents.
    (5) It is part of the Supreme Court.

42. Before 1891, the Supreme Court heard appeals from district trial courts. But in 1891, the circuit courts of appeals were established to

    (1) allow the Supreme Court to concentrate only on the most important cases
    (2) make the states feel more important
    (3) ease the workload of the district trial courts
    (4) provide more jobs for good lawyers
    (5) extend the judicial portion of the checks and balances system of the government

43. As cases are appealed within the jurisdiction in which they were tried, an appeal registered in Chicago by a person who later moved to Indiana would be reviewed by

    (1) the District of Columbia Circuit Court of Appeals
    (2) the Eighth District Circuit Court of Appeals
    (3) the Seventh District Circuit Court of Appeals
    (4) the First District Circuit Court of Appeals
    (5) the Sixth District Circuit Court of Appeals

44. The map supports the conclusion that

    (1) few trial court rulings are ever overturned
    (2) most court cases go uncontested
    (3) the ninth district has more appeals than any other
    (4) a number of people contest the judgment of trial courts
    (5) these federal courts do not hear matrimony or probate cases

Items 45–50 refer to the following graph.

Actual Cost in 1988 for the Registration of a New 1988 Oldsmobile Calais, Model NF1 in Marion County, Indiana

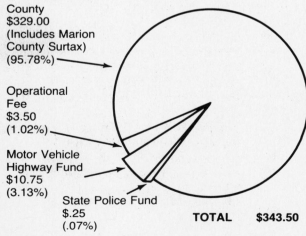

County $329.00 (Includes Marion County Surtax) (95.78%)

Operational Fee $3.50 (1.02%)

Motor Vehicle Highway Fund $10.75 (3.13%)

State Police Fund $.25 (.07%)

TOTAL $343.50

The actual cost of a passenger vehicle registration for Indiana residents is $12.75, which is very low, compared to many states. At the time of registration, excise tax is collected in addition to the registration fee. The taxes are deposited daily in county treasurers' accounts at local financial institutions. County treasurers distribute these monies to local units of government for use by counties, cities, towns, townships, schools, and libraries for a portion of their operational expenses.

45. The major portion of registration for a new car in Marion County, Indiana goes to

    (1) support the state police
    (2) pay off county debts
    (3) small units of government
    (4) the operation of the motor vehicles department
    (5) the state government

46. In comparison to many states, an automobile owner in Indiana pays

    (1) a high excise tax
    (2) a low excise tax
    (3) a high basic registration fee
    (4) a low basic registration fee
    (5) too much to the local county

47. The county most likely charges an excise tax on vehicles because

(1) most people drive cars
(2) counties have few ways to raise revenue
(3) people will pay whether they want to or not
(4) county commissioners want to look good to the state government
(5) people in Indiana all drive expensive new cars

48. It is most likely that the Indiana State Police

(1) rely solely on registration revenues
(2) are funded by sources other than registration fees
(3) strictly enforce prompt payment of fees
(4) assist in the distribution of county monies
(5) favor new registration laws

49. The caption for the graph supports the conclusion that

(1) the operational fee is too low
(2) the percent of excise tax given to the county includes a surtax
(3) not enough money goes to the highway fund
(4) the excise tax is based on the value of the automobile
(5) excise taxes are not charged on cars over ten years old

50. The excise tax charged on automobiles is most similar to

(1) the luxury tax on cigarettes and alcohol
(2) a basic utility bill
(3) an admission fee to an amusement park
(4) the tip one leaves at a restaurant
(5) the bill from a dry cleaning service

51. The United States Congress has joint committees which include members from both the Senate and the House of Representatives. These committees investigate and report on matters that concern both the Senate and the House. One of the most important jobs of a joint committee is to

(1) resolve major differences between the House and Senate over legislation
(2) report on rules and administration
(3) investigate the status of small businesses in the United States
(4) investigate the reasons for the slowdown in space technology
(5) discuss standards of official conduct

Item 52 refers to the following cartoon.

52. The cartoonist is making fun of the cultural assumption that

(1) holding hands is romantic
(2) all types of people have romances
(3) men are stronger than women
(4) behind every strong man is a woman
(5) the army builds more than your character

53. An interesting sociological phenomenon is called cultural lag. This situation exists when belief systems have not kept up with technological change. An example of this occurred in the 1960's when a number of older adults

    (1) refused to believe that a man had landed on the moon even though they saw it on TV
    (2) disapproved of young people demonstrating against the war
    (3) objected to the length of women's skirts
    (4) didn't like the loud music favored by the young
    (5) could hardly believe that a president could be assassinated in our civilized society

54. A fifty-year-old woman has a thirty-year-old daughter who has no social life because she "always has headaches." When it was suggested that the daughter see a psychologist, the mother said, "Never! Insanity doesn't run in my family!" This mother doesn't

    (1) think there is anything wrong with her daughter
    (2) understand what a psychologist actually does
    (3) believe in heredity
    (4) doesn't think psychology is scientific enough
    (5) care what happens to her daughter

55. When a crowd of people starts to react emotionally, it can be transformed from a passive group into an active mob. One common type of mob behavior is aggression. An aggressive mob seeks a target for destruction. An example of aggressive mob behavior in America is

    (1) a sit-in during the sixties
    (2) a rock concert
    (3) the Watts riot of 1967
    (4) the reaction of a crowd at an Indiana basketball game
    (5) a crowd trying to cross 42nd Street in New York City

56. Socialization is the process of learning a group's norms, values, and expectations so that one's behavior is similar to that of everyone else. Conforming to society's norms eventually becomes a habit. Socialization accounts for

    (1) a child's confusion about an adult's requests
    (2) our willingness to stand in line for a movie
    (3) some people's lack of initiative
    (4) the rising crime rate in major cities
    (5) aggressive behavior in congested traffic

57. A person who takes a Rorschach test looks at a series of inkblot designs and describes what each abstract shape represents. Each person who takes such a test describes something different because no two people have the same thoughts or attitudes. Psychologists believe that Rorschach tests can reveal

    (1) how artistic a person is
    (2) intelligence levels
    (3) very little about a person
    (4) characteristics of personality
    (5) a person's cognitive abilities

58. In our youth-oriented society, people tend to associate romance with the young. But researchers have discovered that many people over sixty-five frequently date, are intimate with someone of the opposite sex, and often get married. So the news from psychologists is that

    (1) chivalry is not dead
    (2) romance is better when you're older
    (3) it is better to wait a while before getting married
    (4) older couples just want companionship
    (5) it's never too late to fall in love

The !Kung of the Kalahari Desert are a unique group of people. Archeological evidence suggests they have been in this region of Africa for thousands of years. Anthropological and scientific evidence support the conclusion that they are related to no other race of people.

Despite the fact that their economy is one of hunting and gathering, the !Kung work on the average of only twelve to eighteen hours a week. The !Kung love to hunt and regard it a sport more than subsistence. There are two animals they will not kill for food—the baboon because it looks like a human being, and the hyena because it feeds on human corpses. The diet of the !Kung is primarily vegetarian. A major source of nutrition is the mongongo nut.

The !Kung on the average live longer than Americans. They generally live in small independent camps with no livestock or agriculture and no political organization except for a headman who coordinates the movements of the group. But the headman has no authority to judge or initiate punishment. The !Kung husband and wife both contribute to the maintenance of the household. The female builds the hut and the male makes all the utensils.

The only real threat to the !Kung way of life is the intrusion of civilization into the African desert. Once there were perhaps a hundred !Kung to a group and now there are only three to four families in a group.

59. According to the passage, the !Kung place a high value on

   (1) stability
   (2) organization
   (3) human beings
   (4) authority figures
   (5) the work ethic

60. That the !Kung are unrelated to any other race of people is evidence of

   (1) their successful adaptation to the desert
   (2) the effects of a good diet
   (3) their independent nature
   (4) how unusual they are
   (5) their nomadic lifestyle

61. According to the passage, a hunting and gathering economy is

   (1) best suited for short people
   (2) better than an agricultural economy
   (3) very hard on the hunters
   (4) not necessarily time-consuming
   (5) the only way to live in the Kalahari Desert

62. The reason for the long life span of the !Kung is

   (1) their diet of mongongo nuts
   (2) their innate toughness
   (3) their family harmony
   (4) the absence of meat from their diet
   (5) not specified in the passage

63. If the !Kung had to leave the desert for a town or city, they would most likely

   (1) adapt easily
   (2) become strong political leaders of the community
   (3) begin to have larger families
   (4) feel very confined
   (5) become craftspeople

64. Which of the following terms best describes the culture of the !Kung?

   (1) harmonious
   (2) limited
   (3) perfect
   (4) dysfunctional
   (5) complex

GED Social Studies Test B

Answers and Explanations

1. **(1)** (Analysis) Canada feels that its neighbor is acting irresponsibly. Option (2) is not suggested by the accusation. Option (3) is wrong because it suggests all pollution problems are caused by the United States. Options (4) and (5) have no support in the text.

2. **(2)** (Analysis) The 100°W meridian runs through the major aquifer in the middle of the country. Because to the east of the 100°W meridian there is an abundance of ground water as opposed to the west where there are few aquifers, it can be called the dividing line. Options (1) and (3) are wrong because the meridian does run across the major aquifer. There is no evidence on the map for Options (4) and (5).

3. **(5)** (Comprehension) Only the amount of Myanmar's exports cannot be determined from the map. All the other options can be determined by using the map.

4. **(1)** (Comprehension) That this is a low-census area is stated in the text. Option (2) has no support in the text. Options (3), (4), and (5) are contradicted in the text.

5. **(3)** (Comprehension) Glaciers carved the landscape. There is no support for Options (1), (2), and (4) in the passage. Option (5) is not true.

6. **(3)** (Evaluation) The two praised the land for its farm value. There is no evidence in the passage for Options (1), (2), (4), and (5).

7. **(1)** (Evaluation) The author points out that the residents have taken on the characteristics of the land. Options (2) and (5) are wrong because there is resistance to real estate development here. There is no support in the passage for Option (3). Option (4) is contradicted by the passage.

8. **(2)** (Comprehension) Finger Lakes has remained much the same for two hundred years. Options (1) and (5) are not true. Option (3) is irrelevant. There is no support in the passage for Option (4).

9. **(3)** (Evaluation) This is indicated in the sixth paragraph. Options (2) and (4) are contradicted by the passage. There is no support in the passage for Options (1) and (5).

10. **(1)** (Comprehension) The businesses failed because they had no way to pay their debts. Options (2), (3), and (4) were contributing factors but were not the causes. Option (5) has no support in the passage.

11. **(1)** (Application) When something got in his way, Hitler ignored it. Options (3), (4), and (5) are not true. There is no evidence for Option (2) in the passage.

12. **(2)** (Analysis) Germany had not only lost the war but had also lost a good deal of money. Options (1), (4), and (5) are not true. Option (3) did not occur until after World War II.

13. **(3)** (Evaluation) The Nazi government under Hitler gained control of labor, and afterwards the people had little room to resist. Options (1), (2), and (4) may have some validity, but they are not supported by the passage. There is no evidence in the passage for Option (5).

14. **(5)** (Analysis) Hitler was appointed to the office and was never elected. This eliminates Option (2). Option (1) is wrong because his appointment began in 1933. There is no evidence for Options (3) and (4) in the passage.

15. **(2)** (Application) Threat of a banking failure means loss of deposits. Options (1) and (3) are not true. Options (4) and (5) would not be influenced by the failure of the Kreditanstalt.

16. **(3)** (Comprehension) The disaster was due to a fire. Option (1) is wrong because the blame was assigned only by rumor. Options (2) and (5) contributed to the disaster but were not the cause. There is no support for Option (4) in the passage.

17. **(1)** (Application) Mrs. O'Leary and her cow are traditionally blamed for the Chicago fire. Option (2) was a natural disaster. Options (3) and (5) had identified perpetrators. Option (4) is wrong because the whole system was blamed.

18. **(5)** (Analysis) The occasion of the protest was the accident that resulted in lost lives because only one exit was available. Option (1) might have been a good idea but would be a minor point. There is no evidence for Options (2) and (3) in the passage. Option (4) is wrong because the Irish were still part of the group at this time.

19. **(2)** (Analysis) Immigrants brought their prejudices with them to America. Option (1) is wrong because the feud was not with the Welsh. There is no evidence in the passage for Options (3), (4), and (5).

20. **(3)** (Evaluation) If the group had set the fire as rumored, it would indicate that they would do anything to get at the owners, no matter what cost to the miners inside at the time. Options (1), (2), (4), and (5) were valued by the Molly Maguires.

21. **(5)** (Application) Even though it has never been proven that the tragedy was caused by the Molly Maguires, the tactics were associated with the group. None of the other options are known primarily for their violent, yet furtive, espousal of a cause.

22. **(2)** (Application) The annexation of the territories convinced Americans of their own greatness. Option (1) is not a positive factor. Options (3), (4), and (5) do not have anything to do with the nation becoming a world power.

23. **(4)** (Application) Like the revolutionaries, Southerners found themselves without a say in the government they financially supported. The other options do not apply to the situation.

24. **(2)** (Analysis) With this legislation, the railroads could no longer play favorites or take advantage of the farmers. Option (1) is wrong because regulation is not the same as control. Option (3) is wrong because taxes would be based on total income anyway. There is no basis in the text for Options (4) and (5).

25. **(2)** (Analysis) The increase in literacy would boost newspaper sales. Libraries (Option 1) would not affect newspaper readers. Options (3) and (4) would not have had a great effect. Although Option (5) is true, it would not have influenced the development of newspapers.

26. **(2)** (Application) Planning would assist the consumer in being able to meet payments. Options (1), (3), and (4) would only increase finance charges. Option (5) is wrong because it does not constitute use at all.

27. **(5)** (Analysis) After buying a ticket once a week for five years, the character would have spent much more than $150. Options (1), (2), (3), and (4) are all true but do not really answer the question or apply to this context.

28. **(1)** (Application) The consumer's budget is stretched tight very much like an inflated balloon. If any more pressure is applied, it will burst. Options (2) and (3) are wrong because they refer to the ideas of larger or more intense and not the pressure inside a limited container. Options (4) and (5) are true but do not explain the appropriateness of the word *inflation.*

29. **(4)** (Analysis) If the intent of Congress is to deal with the deficit, legislators should be trying to reduce it and not increase it by voting themselves pay raises. Options (1) and (5) are not true. There is no support in the cartoon for Options (2) and (3).

30. **(4)** (Evaluation) The graph follows no set pattern and shows much fluctuation in construction spending. This information eliminates Option (5). Options (1) and (3) are contradicted by the information on the graph. Option (2) is wrong because the graph does not provide information about what was built.

31. **(3)** (Analysis) The government clearly felt that social programs deserved a larger share of the budget. Because the actual amount of the national debt is not stated, it is impossible to conclude either Option (1) or (2). The information on the graph does not support Options (4) and (5).

32. **(2)** (Application) The two currencies would vary according to national agreement. The exchange rate has little to do with Options (1), (3), and (4). Option (5) might have been somewhat relevant if the businesses wanted payment in dollars.

33. **(2)** (Application) A spiral is implied by the building effect of one thing naturally following another. Options (1), (3), and (4) all concentrate on success. Option (5) only concentrates on failure.

34. **(3)** (Comprehension) Success depends on demand. Success does not depend on the merit of the idea as stated in Option (1). Options (2) and (5) also incorrectly suggest instant success. There is no information in the passage to support Option (4).

35. **(2)** (Application) Without good pastries, there is no chance of a successful pastry shop. Options (1) and (3) have little to do with the situation. Option (4) is illogical. There is no information in the passage to support Option (5).

36. **(5)** (Analysis) They must believe they can succeed. Option (1) is too negative. There is no evidence in the passage for Options (2) and (3). Option (4) may be true, but that's not their assumption.

37. **(2)** (Application) New businesses have no guarantees of success or failure. Option (1) has no support in the passage. Option (3) is wrong because the possibilities are not limited to restaurants. Option (4) is irrelevant. There is no evidence in the passage for Option (5).

38. **(4)** (Evaluation) Food is perishable; stale pastries wouldn't sell, so they must be replaced. The passage does not support any of the other options.

39. **(2)** (Comprehension) California is in the ninth district. Options (1), (3), (4), and (5) are wrong.

40. **(4)** (Analysis) A smaller population would require fewer hearings. There is no support on the map for Options (1), (2), (3), and (5).

41. **(3)** (Analysis) The trial load there is high and results in quite a few appeals. Options (1), (2), (4), and (5) are not true.

42. **(1)** (Analysis) The Supreme Court hears the most important cases and is the final court of appeals; to handle other cases would overburden the Supreme Court. Options (2), (3), and (4) would not necessarily result from the creation of the circuit court system. Option (5) is not possible under the Constitution.

43. **(3)** (Application) Both Chicago and Indiana are in the seventh district. Even if the two were in different districts, a case is appealed in the district in which it was tried. All the other options are wrong.

44. **(4)** (Evaluation) Without people objecting to court rulings, there would be no reason for a court of appeals; so the number of courts reflects the number of appeals. Therefore, Option (2) is wrong. The map does not provide evidence for any of the other options.

45. **(3)** (Comprehension) This is stated in the caption. Therefore, the other options are wrong.

46. **(4)** (Comprehension) This is stated in the caption, so Option (3) is wrong. There is no information on the graph about other states' excise taxes or county appropriations, so Options (1), (2), and (5) are wrong.

47. **(2)** (Analysis) Counties do need to raise money. Options (1) and (3) are true, but they are not reasons for a county tax. There is no evidence to support Option (4). Option (5) is not true.

48. **(2)** (Analysis) If the police relied only on the small percentage as suggested in Option (1), they would be getting very little money. There is no support on the graph for Options (3), (4), or (5).

49. **(4)** (Evaluation) Evidence for this is in the explanation of the figures. Options (1) and (3) are not supported by contrasting figures. Option (2) is wrong because it is a fact and not a conclusion. The caption does not support Option (5).

50. **(1)** (Application) A luxury tax is in addition to the actual cost of the item and goes to funds generally unrelated to the product. Option (2) is wrong because the bill is more like the basic registration fee. Options (3) and (5) have no similarity to the tax. Option (4) is wrong because even though the tip is an addition to the basic bill, it is voluntary.

51. **(1)** (Application) Disagreement between House and Senate would be a matter that would have to be resolved. Although the other options might be handled by a joint committee, none is as important as Option (1).

52. **(3)** (Analysis) While holding hands is romantic, the cartoonist is using the cartoon as a device to reverse our expectations about men's and women's roles. Option (1) is not what the cartoonist is making fun of. Options (2), (4), and (5) are not central to the idea of the cartoon.

53. **(1)** (Application) A disbelief in space technology was expressed despite the publicized existence of that technology. The other options are based on belief systems but have nothing to do with technological progress.

54. **(2)** (Evaluation) The mother is equating psychology with the treatment of insanity. Option (1) is wrong because she probably does think there's something wrong with her daughter. Option (3) is contradicted by the woman's statement. Options (4) and (5) have no support in the passage.

55. **(3)** (Application) In the Watts riot, an entire section of Los Angeles was destroyed out of anger and frustration at racial oppression. Option (1) is wrong because it is a passive group. Options (2) and (4) involve an audience that is expressive but rarely aggressive. Option (5) is wrong because the individuals may be aggressively trying to battle the cars, but they are not a mob nor are they seeking a target for destruction.

56. **(2)** (Application) Standing in line is an accepted norm. Options (1) and (3) are not related to socialization but to learning and personality. Options (4) and (5) are wrong because they are examples of departures from social norms.

57. **(4)** (Evaluation) Expression of thoughts and attitudes reveals something about personality. Options (1), (2), (3), and (5) are not discovered through inkblots.

58. **(5)** (Comprehension) The message is that older adults fall in love, too. Although Options (1), (2), and (3) may be true, they are not the main idea of the passage. Option (4) is wrong because, according to the passage, older couples obviously want more than companionship.

59. **(3)** (Evaluation) This is supported by the information in the passage about the !Kung taboo on killing baboons and hyenas. The other options are things the !Kung care little about.

60. **(4)** (Analysis) This conclusion is supported by the evidence in the passage. None of the other options have anything to do with racial distinctions.

61. **(4)** (Comprehension) This is stated in the passage. Option (3) is not true. There is no evidence in the passage for Options (1), (2), and (5).

62. **(5)** (Comprehension) The passage does not give a reason for the life span.

63. **(4)** (Application) Their attitudes and lifestyle are not suited to city life, so Options (1) and (2) are wrong. There is no reason to assume either Option (4) or (5) as there is no information about these aspects in the passage.

64. **(1)** (Application) The !Kung appear to get along well with each other and nature. There is no evidence in the passage to support Options (2), (3), and (5). Option (4) is wrong because it is the opposite of how the !Kung are described in the passage.

Analysis of Performance on the Simulated GED Social Studies Test B

The chart below will help you determine your strengths and weaknesses in reading comprehension and in the social studies content areas of geography, history, economics, political science, and behavioral science.

Directions

Circle the number of each item that you answered correctly on the Simulated GED Test B. Count the number of items you answered correctly in each column. Write the amount in the <u>total correct</u> space of each column. (For example, if you answered 8 history items correctly, place the number 8 in the blank before <u>out of 16</u>.) Complete this process for the remaining columns.

Count the number of items you answered correctly in each row. Write that amount in the <u>total correct</u> space of each row. (For example, in the <u>comprehension</u> row, write the number correct in the blank before <u>out of 13</u>.) Complete this process for the remaining rows.

Test B Analysis of Performance Chart

Item Types:	Geography (p. 12–37)	History (p. 38–77)	Economics (p. 78–103)	Political Science (p. 104–135)	Behavioral Science (p. 136–153)	Total Correct
Comprehension	③, 4, 5, 7	10, 16	34	㊴, ㊺, ㊻,	58, 61, 62	_____ out of 13
Analysis	1, ②	12, 14, 18, 19, 24, ㉕	㉗, ㉙, ㉛, 36	㊵, ㊶, ㊷, ㊼, ㊽	㊼, 60	_____ out of 19
Application		11, 15, 17, 21, 22, 23	26, 28, 32, 33, 35, 37	㊸, ㊿, 51	53, 55, 56, 63, 64	_____ out of 20
Evaluation	6, 8, 9	13, 20	㉚, 38	㊹, ㊾	54, 57, 59	_____ out of 12
Total Correct	_____ out of 9	_____ out of 16	_____ out of 13	_____ out of 13	_____ out of 13	Total correct: _____ out of 64 1-50 = Need More Review 51-64 = Congratulations! You're ready!

(Circled items indicate those questions with a graphic stimulus.)

If you answered fewer than 50 of the 64 questions correctly, determine which areas are hardest for you. Go back to the *Steck-Vaughn GED Social Studies* book and review the content in those areas.

In the parentheses under the heading, the page numbers tell you where you can find the beginning of specific instruction about that area of social studies in the *Steck-Vaughn GED Social Studies* book. Also refer to the chart on page 3.

ANSWERS & EXPLANATIONS PRACTICE EXERCISES

Chapter 1: Geography (Pages 4–14)

1. **(4)** (Comprehension) If Denver had an adequate water supply, it would not need to divert water. Option (1) is incorrect because only the habitat is in danger, not the birds themselves. There is no evidence in the passage for Options (2) or (3). Option (5) is wrong because the dispute is based on whether this statement is true.

2. **(3)** (Application) The abuse of water systems would seriously affect the environment. Option (1) incorrectly suggests expansion, not maintenance, of water-poor cities. Options (2), (4), and (5) have no support in the passage.

3. **(1)** (Analysis) The planners would be rightly concerned with people and believe the birds could land elsewhere, but Option (2) would not convince the environmentalists. Option (3) suggests a wasteful use of water. Option (4) is false. Option (5) would involve persuading the cranes to go along with the decision.

4. **(2)** (Comprehension) Stopping construction would prevent the threat. Option (1) suggests environmentalists would give up their beliefs. Options (3) and (5) make little sense. Option (4) is incorrect because the problem is not cruelty but a difference in priorities.

5. **(2)** (Comprehension) Arizona is known to be warm and dry, and the majority of Sun City's population is over the age of 60. There is no support for Options (1), (3), or (5). Option (4) is unlikely because of the age of most of the population.

6. **(3)** (Application) With a population that consists mainly of senior citizens, the city would be prepared for a number of medical problems. Options (1), (2), and (4) would have few users. Option (5) would not be as necessary as Option (3).

7. **(4)** (Application) Hurricane winds would cause more damage to Options (2), (3), and (5) than to low buildings. Option (1) is incorrect because the flooding would turn dirt floor cellars into swamps.

8. **(2)** (Analysis) Although Great Britain is separated from the continent by water (Option 5), western Europe is only about half the size of the United States, making international shipping fairly easy. There is no evidence for Options (1) or (4) in the text. Although Option (3) is true, it has nothing to do with the Common Market.

9. **(4)** (Comprehension) The natural boundary between these states is the Mississippi River. The other options are true.

10. **(4)** (Application) Cairo is the only city that has access to two river systems.

11. **(4)** (Comprehension) Greenwich is at the Prime Meridian from which all longitude is measured; therefore, it would be 0° longitude. The Equator is 0° latitude.

12. **(3)** (Application) Latitude and longitude would provide points of reference on the vastness of the ocean. Option (1) would involve knowledge of the course of the river, not other coordinates. Each of the other options involves too limited an area.

13. **(3)** (Comprehension) Brunei lies outside the borders of Malaysia; it is another country. The other options are marked as cities on the map.

14. **(4)** (Application) Indonesia shares a border with East Malaysia; this would offer easy access for trade. The other options would involve sea or air transportation.

15. **(2)** (Evaluation) The government would be in constant conflict with the rest of the nation, so attaining independence would ease tensions. Option (1) is irrelevant. Options (3) and (5) have no geographic support. There is no evidence for Option (4) on the map.

16. **(5)** (Analysis) Muslims do not eat pork (Option 3), and Hindus do not eat beef (Option 2); but a primary protein source is available to all Malaysians in the surrounding ocean. Neither Option (1) nor Option (4) is a major source of protein.

17. **(1)** (Comprehension) Being able to get places quickly would create a new point of view. Option (2) has no support in the passage. Options (3), (4), and (5) are based on a misreading of the necessary distortion in the diagram.

18. **(3)** (Application) Advances in technology have shortened flight times. There is no support for the other options in the diagram.

19. **(2)** (Analysis) Although Option (1) is true, Option (2) would be more likely to influence an increase in defense. There is no evidence on the diagram for Options (3) or (4). Option (5) is not indicated on the diagram.

20. **(2)** (Application) The time has passed when geographical factors limited the way wars were fought. In order to avoid total destruction, world powers must focus on peace. There is no basis for Options (1) or (3), and Options (4) and (5) are not logical conclusions.

21. **(4)** (Comprehension) Option (4) is the only option that is not concerned with the population.

22. **(2)** (Analysis) A replacement for fossil fuel would eliminate the problem. Option (1) still suggests using a fossil fuel. Options (3) and (4) are incorrect because they treat the symptoms and not the source. Option (5) does not deal with the problem at all.

23. **(3)** (Comprehension) Russia is just across the Bering Strait from Alaska. Option (1) is irrelevant. Option (2) is contradicted by a joint claim of the Oregon Territory. Option (4) assumes a political situation that did not develop until the twentieth century. There is no support for Option (5) on the map.

24. **(4)** (Analysis) The area that became California was claimed by Spain. There is no support for Options (1) and (5) on the map. Option (2) is incorrect because France had not yet acquired the Louisiana Territory. Option (3) refers to a later development.

25. **(3)** (Comprehension) Most of the dots are located either in the ocean areas or on land near the oceans. There is no evidence for the other options on the map.

26. **(5)** (Application) Acapulco, Mexico is located on the Pacific coastline where earthquakes are concentrated. All the other options are not near the earthquake patterns.

27. **(2)** (Analysis) The Bureau of Land Management is concerned with conservation and would realize that recycling might reduce some of the logging in areas already stricken by forest fires. Options (1), (3), and (4) are true but do not explain the Bureau of Land Management's interest in recycling paper. There is no evidence for Option (5) in the passage.

28. **(3)** (Evaluation) The passage mentions the heavy rains in the west but does not refer to forest fires (Option 1) or animals (Option 2). There is no support for Options (4) or (5) in the passage.

29. **(4)** (Comprehension) The mountains tend to turn the ocean air currents back into the western valley. Option (1) would not affect humidity, and Option (2) is a result of the dryness. There is no support for Options (4) or (5) in the passage.

30. **(5)** (Application) Eastern Oregon borders on Idaho and would probably have similar crops. Options (3) and (4) are incorrect because they are midwestern states.

31. **(4)** (Comprehension) The percentages rise and fall slightly. There is no evidence on the chart for the other options.

32. **(2)** (Analysis) The percentages for small towns and rural areas show a decrease which would account for the stable percentages in the cities. People from small towns and rural areas were moving to the cities to find work. Option (1) would affect all areas of population, not just the city. Options (3), (4), and (5) do not explain the figures for the cities.

33. **(1)** (Application) City officials would probably have the same concerns as always, but the other groups experienced a boom in business because of the development of the suburban areas.

34. **(2)** (Application) The population in the suburbs increased by 7% between 1950 and 1960 and again by 1970. This rate would probably slow within 30 years, but an increase of 17.7% would not be surprising. Options (1) and (5) are wrong because they reflect little change. Options (3) and (4) are wrong because they reverse the trend shown.

35. **(1)** (Evaluation) The oil spill is a threat to the ecological balance which affects all nations; assistance from a nation mainly regarded as a political enemy shows an understanding of the serious nature of the problem. But this does not suggest that Option (5) is true; differences are set aside, not settled. There is insufficient support in the text for Options (2), (3), and (4).

36. **(4)** (Evaluation) The other side of the equation must be known. Only Japan's imports for 1988 are given. The other options do not supply relevant information.

37. **(5)** (Evaluation) A mileage or distance scale is missing from the map. All other options can be determined from the information provided.

38. **(4)** (Evaluation) The only way the Pacific end can be east of the Atlantic end is if the canal runs from the northwest in the Atlantic to the southeast in the Pacific. This is possible because Panama's length runs east to west, or parallel to the Equator. Options (1) and (2) are geographically false. Option (3) would make the statement impossible. There is no evidence in the text for Option (5).

39. **(1)** (Analysis) An ethnic group is a national or cultural group. A variety of ethnic groups would result from immigration from the whole of Europe. Prior to this period, the majority of the city populations were from northwestern Europe. Option (2) is too limited by cultural group and time frame. Option (3) refers to a result of the mass immigration. Option (4) is not an explanation of diversity. Evidence for Option (5) is not available on the map, but the railroad construction would have been far from the cities.

40. **(2)** (Analysis) Because Italy is a major country in southern Europe, it is reasonable to assume that a large percentage of the immigrants were Italian. Options (1) and (5) offer no basis for the statement. Option (3) refers to the wrong area, and Option (4) refers to inaccurate information.

41. **(3)** (Application) The Statue of Liberty is a symbol of hope and refuge. Options (1), (2), (4), and (5) represent specific historical events and persons rather than a general ideal.

42. **(2)** (Evaluation) Most of the immigrants during this time did not speak English. Because the previous twenty years brought an influx of immigrants into American cities, there was little skilled employment available. The map does not support Option (1). There is no evidence for Options (3), (4), or (5) on the map.

Chapter 2: History (Pages 15–25)

1. **(3)** (Evaluation) Four of the explorers listed were Italian. Option (1) is wrong because Columbus was looking for the Far East, not a new continent. There is no evidence in the passage for Options (2) or (4). Option (5) is true, but the passage only suggests that the Altantic Ocean lies between Europe and the Americas.

2. **(3)** (Comprehension) Because more exploration was done by Spain, that country claimed the most territory. There is no evidence for Options (1) or (2) in the passage. Option (4) is wrong because Columbus claimed only the West Indies. Option (5) is wrong because the explorers did not cross paths.

3. **(1)** (Analysis) The French colonized the Canadian Territory, the Dutch colonized the Hudson River area, and the Spanish colonized the South American region. There is no support for Options (2), (4), or (5) in the passage. Option (3) is false.

4. **(2)** (Analysis) Both Cabot and Columbus reached only outlying islands of the lands. Options (1) and (4) would have no influence on what the new land was called. Option (3) does not explain why Spain didn't choose its first explorer. Option (5) is false.

5. **(2)** (Comprehension) All options except Option (2) are stated in the passage. Political independence was not yet an issue.

6. **(2)** (Analysis) Option (2) provides a sound economic reason. There is no support for Option (1) in the passage; being in debtor's prison is not the same as being a fugitive. There is no evidence in the passage for Options (3) and (5). Option (4) may have been true for some people but does not explain why they went to America.

7. **(2)** (Comprehension) As the land was claimed by the country, settlement could occur only with government approval. Options (1) and (2) have no support in the passage. Option (4) is true but has nothing to do with systematic colonization. Option (5) was not quite true.

8. **(2)** (Comprehension) Locke believed the government should not interfere with private property. There is no support for Options (1) or (5). Options (3) and (4) are contradicted by the passage.

9. **(1)** (Application) Locke would support the colonists' objection of an invasion of their private property. Options (2), (3), and (5) are not relevant to the violation of citizens' rights. Locke would not have supported Option (4).

10. **(2)** (Application) Proper representation was one of Locke's points. Although the other options are phrases associated with the American Revolution, they do not reflect the philosopher's beliefs.

11. **(1)** (Evaluation) Locke would be most concerned with the issue. Option (3) is a logical fallacy. There is no support for Options (2), (4), and (5) in the passage.

12. **(4)** (Comprehension) Only statistics for Option (4) are given. Statistics for Options (1), (2), and (3) are not given. There is no support for Option (5) on the graph.

13. **(1)** (Evaluation) This is a comment on what people can do with very few resources. There is no evidence for Options (2), (3), and (5). Option (4) is wrong because it is false and lacks evidence.

14. **(3)** (Application) The casualties of the Civil War were staggering. The death tolls have nothing to do with Options (1), (2), or (4). Option (5) is unclear.

15. **(2)** (Application) There is no evidence for Options (1) and (3) on the graph. Options (4) and (5) would have no bearing on the effect of the losses.

16. **(4)** (Evaluation) Death tolls do not reflect the importance of a war. Option (1) is wrong because the total can be figured. There is no support for Options (2) or (3) on the graph. Option (5) is eliminated because Option (4) is the correct answer.

17. **(1)** (Analysis) The large number of lives lost would have an adverse effect on the labor force but would not result in the other options.

18. **(3)** (Comprehension) Although only craftspeople and farmers are discussed in this passage, there is an implication that other occupations were affected. Options (1) and (2) contradict the information given. Options (4) and (5) have no support in the passage.

19. **(4)** (Analysis) Options (1) and (2) have no support in the passage. Although Options (3) and (5) might be true, neither was discussed or implied in the passage.

20. **(5)** (Comprehension) There is no evidence that all farmers turned to cash crops. Options (1), (2), (3), and (4) are not suggested in the passage.

21. **(3)** (Application) Computer technology has changed many facets of everyday life because it has required retraining or relocation for employment and has made a number of products available to people who previously could not afford them. Options (1), (2), (4), and (5) have not affected as many people as Option (3).

22. **(3)** (Evaluation) An agrarian economy requires a large rural population, and an industrial economy requires a large urban population. Although Option (1) is true, no figures are given for the origins of the growing urban population. There is no evidence on the graph for Option (2). Options (4) and (5) are incorrect according to the graph.

23. **(2)** (Application) Machines are used to manufacture items in the same way that political machines produced the desired number of votes by buying them. The other options may be true, but they do not suggest a mechanical process.

24. **(3)** (Analysis) Political machines were interested in money and power, and they would turn a blind eye if the price was right. There is not enough evidence for Options (1), (2), or (4) in the passage. Option (5) is unlikely because the political machines were too powerful.

25. **(3)** (Analysis) The weight of skyscrapers combined with the removal of the natural support of earth is suggested as the cause of collapse. Option (1) might apply to San Francisco but is not supported in the cartoon. Options (2) and (5) are not suggested in the cartoon. Option (4) may be the reason for the building of skyscrapers, but it is not the direct cause for the sinking of the city.

26. **(1)** (Analysis) City growth is usually considered to be progress, but in the cartoon it is interpreted as a destructive force. Options (2) and (3) refer to minor elements of the cartoon, not to the opinion they convey. Option (4) is too general. There is no evidence in the cartoon for Option (5).

27. **(1)** (Application) The main idea of the cartoon is that there are too many outdoor advertising signs cluttering the cityscape solely in the interest of making money. There is no support for Options (2) and (3) in the cartoon. Option (4) is wrong because the implication is that the signs are not really art. Option (5) may be an indirect cause of the use of signs, but it is not the focus of the cartoon.

28. **(3)** (Comprehension) The dollar sign on the bag indicates money. The fact that it is tied to both buildings and signs represents that it is related to advertising. Option (2) ignores the cartoon's main concern. There is no evidence for Options (1), (4), and (5) in the cartoon.

29. **(1)** (Application) The phrase captures the idea of a woman working in a tough job that is especially important to the war effort. Options (2) and (4) are incorrect because they emphasize the domestic role of women. Option (3) is not a reflection of the importance of these women. Option (5) is wrong because Carry Nation was a temperance crusader in the 1800's.

30. **(3)** (Analysis) The women realized that equal work deserved equal pay. There is no evidence for Options (1) and (2) in the passage. Options (4) and (5) do not explain the women's dissatisfaction.

31. **(4)** (Comprehension) The boy wearing dark glasses does not know the simple fact that a half dozen is six; this eliminates Option (5). There is not enough evidence in the cartoon for Option (1). There is no support in the cartoon for Option (2). Wearing headphones is not sufficient to suggest Option (3).

32. **(2)** (Analysis) The notice implies that American students are being ranked against students from other countries and are doing poorly in contrast. Math and science are central to a highly technological society, so Options (1), (4), and (5) are wrong. There is no evidence for Option (3) in the cartoon.

33. **(1)** (Analysis) Historical events affect culture and social activity, and are, therefore, more than dry facts. There is no support in this passage for Options (2) and (5). Option (3) may be true occasionally but not always. Option (4) is logically incorrect; the events in themselves are not symbols.

34. **(3)** (Application) Much of the music dealt in some way with the concepts of life, liberty, and the pursuit of happiness. Options (1) and (2) are contradicted by evidence in the passage. There is no support for Options (4) and (5) in the passage.

35. **(1)** (Application) Political values can be shaped by a cultural medium. Although some people might like to believe Options (2), (3), and (4), none are true. Option (5) is wrong because this period was not one of innocence.

36. **(2)** (Evaluation) Most of the discussion concerns reactions to political situations. There is no evidence for Options (1) and (2) in the passage. Option (4) is eliminated by the reference to the patriotic song by Sadler. Dylan's songs of social protest eliminate Option (5).

37. **(5)** (Application) The visit was most likely an indication of a desire for better international relations. Option (1) is wrong because it assumes a faulty cause and effect. There is no evidence for Options (2) and (3) in the text. Option (4) is wrong because a visit is not usually hostile.

38. (2) (Comprehension) Several views of history are mentioned. The other options are not supported by the passage.

39. (4) (Analysis) The implication is that people either did not pay attention to or did not learn from past events and made the same mistakes. Options (1), (3), and (5) are true but are not related to the suggestion. Option (2) is true only in some cases and is not a result of the suggestion.

40. (3) (Comprehension) The phrase suggests that today's newsworthy events will be less newsworthy tomorrow. The other options are not true.

41. (2) (Application) With additional information, the historical view of this event will have changed, and the record of it will have been revised. Options (1), (3), and (4) are not concerned with the new perspective. Option (5) is wrong because it assumes no further information can be discovered.

42. (5) (Evaluation) It is suggested that understanding how the past affects the present will give insight into how to plan for the future. Although Options (1), (2), (3), and (4) are often true, they are only aspects of the recording and understanding of the historical process.

43. (3) (Application) The assassination of two charismatic and influential presidents within 100 years of one another appears to be repetition. Option (1) is wrong because the wars were between different political bodies and for different causes. Options (2) and (4) are about unrelated events. Option (5) is wrong because the election of a president is an expected event.

44. (1) (Comprehension) This option summarizes the intent of the majority of New Deal programs. Option (2) has no support in the passage. Options (3), (4), and (5) are wrong because they are all only aspects of Option (1).

45. (3) (Analysis) Only Option (3) does not limit the freedom of choice for either the individual or the state. All the other options are examples of government restrictions and intervention.

46. (2) (Comprehension) The jumble of initials gives the impression of an alphabet soup. There is no support for Options (1), (2), and (4) in the passage. Option (5) is probably true, but it is not a reason for the nickname.

47. (4) (Evaluation) Government funding means government spending. None of the other options are related to the financial situation of the government itself.

Chapter 3: Economics (Pages 26–35)

1. **(2)** (Comprehension) The total aid to Asia is almost 75% of the total donation. Options (1) and (3) are wrong because actual figures are not given, only percentages of an unspecified total donation. There is no evidence for Option (4) on the graph. Option (5) is incorrect because the United States donates more.

2. **(3)** (Comprehension) The fact that both nations provide foreign aid indicates a concern for developing nations. Options (1) and (5) are wrong because there is no information on the graph concerning actual need. Option (2) is wrong because there is no indication of competition. Although Option (4) might have some basis, no evidence is provided on the graph.

3. **(2)** (Comprehension) Options (1) and (3) are wrong because they are based on a misreading of the text. Option (4) is wrong because some solutions are found. Option (5) does not answer the question. Evidence for the correct option is in the second paragraph.

4. **(5)** (Application) Balancing the national budget without additional taxation is the only complex economic problem not mentioned in the passage. Options (1) and (4) are not complex problems of economics. Options (2) and (3) are wrong because they are examples already provided by the author.

5. **(2)** (Analysis) The author believes that economists have the tools to avoid depressions, but this has not been proven. The other options are facts.

6. **(4)** (Evaluation) Economic study relies on data from the other social sciences. The passage does not support Options (1) and (3) and contradicts Option (2). Option (5) is an incorrect conclusion.

7. **(2)** (Comprehension) The deficit is a serious drain on federal resources. It is not a joke as suggested by Option (1), nor is it easily resolved as suggested by Option (5). Neither Option (3) nor Option (4) is suggested in the cartoon.

8. **(3)** (Analysis) Throwing good money after bad is a waste and a thoughtless gamble. The other options are all too positive.

9. **(3)** (Application) Selling her part of the business would include settlements for the distribution of profit and debt. Both partners are responsible until the partnership is dissolved; therefore, Options (1) and (2) are false. Neither Option (4) nor Option (5) affects the legal partnership.

10. **(4)** (Application) A bank may have reservations about lending a large sum of money to an individual because only one person bears the responsibility of repayment. Options (1) and (2) are wrong because they are benefits and not problems. The problems in Options (3) and (5) apply to any business, not just a sole proprietorship.

11. **(3)** (Analysis) Because a corporation is a separate legal entity, it would not be affected as stated in Options (1) and (5). Individual ownership of stock eliminates the possibility of Options (2) and (4) because ownership extends to the stock alone.

12. **(1)** (Evaluation) A corporation involves more legal work, and with a number of owners, a more complex management arrangement than the other types of business. No evidence is provided in the definitions for Options (2), (3), (4), and (5).

13. **(4)** (Application) This is not an example of an economic principle. Options (1), (2), (3), and (4) are based on people buying more when prices are low and less when prices are high.

14. **(5)** (Analysis) This would result in more profit. Options (1) and (4) would lower profits. Option (2) might be risky, and Option (3) would not improve the business.

15. **(2)** (Comprehension) The increases in all three cases are at least 10%. Option (1) is false. Options (3) and (4) are wrong because there is no mention of who pays what percentage. There is no evidence for Option (5) on the graph.

16. **(2)** (Application) Employers, most of whom want to save money, would decrease their contributions. Option (1) is not likely. Options (3) and (5) would not affect the percentage of benefit payments. Option (4) would make the jobs less worthwhile.

17. **(1)** (Analysis) The increase in the cost of medical treatment is directly related to the problem. Option (2) has nothing to do with basic health insurance. Options (3), (4), and (5) may be true, but they are not the direct causes of cost increase.

18. **(3)** (Evaluation) An increase of 10% during one year is regarded as excessive and inflationary. Although Options (1) and (2) may be true, they are not supported by facts in the chart. There is no evidence for Option (4) in the chart. Option (5) is contradicted by the figures.

19. **(2)** (Analysis) The author assumes that a product that is not made is not missed. Options (1) and (3) are the opposite of this assumption. There is no support for Options (4) and (5) in the passage.

20. **(5)** (Analysis) A less capitalistic society is not mentioned in the passage. Options (1), (2), (3), and (4) are mentioned as results of low productivity.

21. **(1)** (Analysis) The only item listed that the United States does not import is wheat. In fact, it is in such abundance that it is exported. All the other options refer to items the United States imports in quantity because home productivity is low.

22. **(2)** (Evaluation) The author is not concerned with individual products but with the result of economic security. Option (1) is not supported with facts. Option (3) is wrong because it deals with values instead of economics. Option (4) is not suggested by the passage. And Option (5) is wrong because the author sees capacity production as a foundation and not a cure-all.

23. **(3)** (Comprehension) The cartoon suggests that the savings and loan institution would accept financial help. The word *donation* does not imply a regular charity as suggested by Option (1). Options (2), (4), and (5) are not supported in the cartoon.

24. **(1)** (Analysis) The substitution of the word *donation* for *withdrawal* is what makes the cartoon both funny and analytical. The other options are not related to the phrase.

25. **(2)** (Analysis) This assumption is essential to understanding the cartoon. Options (1), (3), and (5) are not important to an understanding of the cartoon. Option (4) is false.

26. **(2)** (Evaluation) There is not enough evidence for Options (1), (3), or (5) in the cartoon. The cobweb suggests lack of use but cannot be taken literally as a sign that the streets are actually dirty as implied by Option (4).

27. **(4)** (Comprehension) Options (1), (2), and (3) are wrong because they all decreased. Option (5) is not given on the chart.

28. **(2)** (Analysis) If the unemployment rate has decreased, more people have jobs, and therefore, more money. There is no real support for Options (1) and (4). Option (3) suggests a faulty cause and effect. Option (5) is wrong because home sales are down.

29. **(1)** (Comprehension) The evidence of the picket sign supports Option (1). There is no support in the cartoon for the other options.

30. **(3)** (Evaluation) It is evident that the baggage handlers are not in sympathy with the strikers. Option (1) is wrong because only the strikers have a gripe. There is no evidence for Options (2), (4), or (5) in the cartoon.

31. **(4)** (Application) Option (4) is possible according to the figures on the graphs. Options (1) and (2) are not supported by facts on the graphs. Option (3) is wrong because there is no information about specific dollar figures. The passage of time does not suggest Option (5).

32. **(4)** (Analysis) A drop in productivity would result in inflation and would affect earnings. Option (1) is unlikely, and Option (2) would result in higher earnings. There is no evidence in the graphs for Option (3). Option (5) would not decrease wages, but it would decrease net income.

33. **(1)** (Application) A continued drop in the value of money would result in less buying power. The correct option eliminates Options (2), (3), and (4). Option (5) is too extreme.

34. **(2)** (Evaluation) The rates in the two graphs follow unequal paths, but both reflect the influence of inflation. Options (4) and (5) are not supported by the information on the graphs. There is no evidence on the graphs for Option (1). Option (3) is wrong because the value of wages has begun to decrease as spending continues to increase.

35. **(3)** (Application) Only lumber is found in nature. Option (1) is labor. Options (2), (4), and (5) are capital.

36. **(1)** (Application) Chemicals would be the primary expense. Options (2), (3), and (5) would have no expenses for natural resources; all their materials would be produced beforehand. Even the paper used by a publishing house would have come from another company. Option (4) is wrong because the major expense would be labor.

37. **(1)** (Comprehension) The comment describes the investment firm's opinion of the potential customer and suggests how easy it would be to get her to invest. The other options are not clearly supported in the cartoon.

38. **(4)** (Application) The cartoonist objects to institutions taking advantage of people, senior citizens in particular, by playing on their fears for the future. There is no evidence for Options (1), (2), or (3) in the cartoon. Because Option (4) is correct, Option (5) is eliminated.

Chapter 4: Political Science (Pages 36–46)

1. **(3)** (Application) The Food and Drug Administration prevents the sale of impure or adulterated food, drugs, and cosmetics. Options (1) and (2) are incorrect because they are international political organizations. Options (4) and (5) are not protective agencies.

2. **(1)** (Application) Laws set limits on behavior and help to prevent infringement on rights. Options (2), (3), and (5) have no legal effect. Option (4) may lead to a law but does not ensure anything.

3. **(1)** (Analysis) A government structure can regulate the exchange of goods and services. Options (2), (4), and (5) are wrong because liberty, dependence, and independence are all limited within a social structure. Option (3) is not a primary government concern.

4. **(3)** (Evaluation) People can rarely provide for all their own needs, and within a complex society, they require the organization of a government. Options (1) and (2) do not apply to the need for structure. Options (4) and (5) are not true.

5. **(2)** (Comprehension) Equality is used in a general sense of all individuals being human and having the same rights. Options (1), (3), and (5) are wrong because equal does not mean identical. Option (4) is a denial of basic rights.

6. **(3)** (Evaluation) None of the principles can be proven; thus, Option (1) is eliminated. Options (4) and (5) are also based on belief and not fact. Option (2) is not suggested in the text.

7. **(4)** (Application) A law can be questioned because there is no absolute truth, and people have the right to make choices. Options (1), (2), (3), and (5) violate the rights of others.

8. **(5)** (Analysis) Option (5) is primarily concerned more with generalities and a review of past performance. Options (1) and (2) are based on the principles of democracy. Option (3) is wrong because the separation allows freedom of choice and respect for an individual. Option (4) is wrong because these laws are based on the concept of equality.

9. **(3)** (Comprehension) The labels on the briefcases refer to elements in a speech that should not have to be provided for the speaker. Option (1) is not an opinion. Options (2), (4), and (5) may be true but are not suggested in this cartoon.

10. **(4)** (Application) The cartoon implies that the candidates are following scripts rather than listening to and refuting each other's arguments. Although Options (1) and (2) might be true generally, there is not enough support to suggest the cartoonist agrees. Options (3) and (5) are not supported by the cartoon.

11. **(3)** (Comprehension) Right to counsel is guaranteed. A poor person probably could not afford to hire a lawyer. Options (1), (2), and (5) are not mentioned in the passage. Option (4) is wrong because the actual length of time is not specified.

12. **(3)** (Analysis) When the Sixth Amendment was written, there were no TVs or radios or even news reporters. Today the public can form an opinion even before a case is tried. There is no support for the other options; none of them would affect impartiality.

13. **(5)** (Application) The Sixth Amendment was written to prevent unfair treatment of the accused. Options (1), (2), and (3) are not addressed by the amendment. Option (4) is incorrect because only aspects of the process are mentioned.

14. **(3)** (Evaluation) Only if the accused is able to present a defense can unjust imprisonment be avoided. Options (1) and (2) cannot be prevented by law. There is no evidence for Options (4) and (5) in the passage.

15. **(3)** (Analysis) The cartoonist is suggesting that some people regard response to a poll as equal to voting even though polls have no effect on the outcome of an election. Options (1), (2), and (5) are wrong because only a vote affects the political process. There is no evidence for Option (4) in the cartoon.

16. **(1)** (Analysis) Confusion about the importance of an opinion poll indicates a misunderstanding of the political process. The cartoonist may believe Option (4), but in this cartoon the focus is on the attitude of the public and not the worth of a poll. Option (3) is false. There is insufficient evidence in the cartoon for Options (2) and (5), but they are also unlikely considering the nature of the cartoon.

17. **(3)** (Analysis) A third party on a ballot means that enough people were not happy with the other choices. Options (1) and (5) are wrong because the inclusion is evidence of change instead of decay. There is not enough support for Options (2) and (4) in the text.

18. **(2)** (Application) The company is trying to persuade through pressure, a common and legal practice. Therefore, Options (1) and (5) are wrong. There is no support for Option (3) in the text. Option (4) is wrong because it does not refer to the group's action.

19. **(4)** (Evaluation) Only a desire for change is suggested in the passage. The specific goals of the students are not mentioned or implied; therefore, the other options are eliminated.

20. **(3)** (Application) Khomeini ruled mainly by virtue of his powerful personality. The other options are examples of rule by legal-rational authority.

21. **(2)** (Analysis) Although all the other options are often true, what makes the government unstable is that it is held together because of the personality of one person. When that person is no longer in charge, the basis for rule disappears.

22. **(4)** (Application) Leadership in a monarchy is usually attained by inheritance or through marriage to a member of the royal family. Leadership in the other options is achieved through election, appointment, or by overthrowing the previous government.

23. **(1)** (Evaluation) The obligations of the officials are defined by laws. Options (2) and (3) are eliminated by Option (1). Options (4) and (5) are not suggested or supported by the definitions.

24. **(4)** (Comprehension) The law concerns people the president can designate to act for him or her. The law does not limit the president's responsibilities as suggested in Option (1) or add to the duties of the president as suggested by Option (2). The president is still responsible for all who act for him, so Option (3) is wrong. The law relieves the president of some duties but not all of them as stated in Option (5).

25. **(1)** (Evaluation) Some of the duties listed in the passage cover a wide range of abilities. The suggestion that an ordinary person would break under the stress of the office eliminates Options (2) and (4). There is no support in the passage for Option (3) except for minor functions. Option (5) may be true of some duties, but some also appear fairly ordinary.

26. **(4)** (Application) Wilson implies that only extraordinary people could handle the demands of the presidency if the task isn't lightened a bit. Candidates would have to be exceptionally intelligent and strong. Options (1), (2), and (3) are characters who break under the strain. Option (5) only has strength.

27. **(2)** (Application) The president must be familiar with all aspects of the job and with the details in order to make the major decisions. Options (1) and (4) contradict this idea. Option (3) is wrong because some balance is needed. There is no support for Option (5) in the passage.

28. **(1)** (Comprehension) Pennsylvania, Maryland, and North Carolina split their votes. The other options are incorrect.

29. **(3)** (Analysis) By casting a vote for Jay, Federalists made sure Adams had one more vote than Pickney. There is insufficient evidence for the other options. Option (4) is incorrect because there is no evidence of who voted for Jay.

30. **(5)** (Evaluation) Indiana is clearly marked as a territory; only states voted. There is no support for Option (1) by the facts on the map. Option (2) is wrong because New England was solidly behind Adams. Options (3) and (4) are wrong because there is no information about the popular vote on the map.

31. **(3)** (Evaluation) Because Jefferson and Burr received the same number of votes, either one could become president. The map does not have the information of who did become president. All of the other options are on the map.

32. **(4)** (Application) The knowledge and concern for constitutional issues suggest that the author is involved in law. Option (1) is incorrect because a protester would not be so objective. Options (2) and (3) are wrong because neither would be likely to have the knowledge nor the need to refrain from discussing a court case. Option (5) is wrong because the author clearly places value on the constitution.

33. **(2)** (Comprehension) This is suggested in the last sentence. Options (1), (3), and (4) are contradicted by evidence in the passage. Option (5) is wrong as the act was seen as dissent but not one protected under current law.

34. **(5)** (Evaluation) By ruling that the First Amendment guarantees of free speech protect those who burn the flag in political protest, the Supreme Court challenged the existing laws, contrary to the author's expectation. Options (1), (3), and (4) are not opinions of the author. Option (2) is an opinion of the author but was not contradicted by the Supreme Court.

35. **(2)** (Application) These laws violated the concept of equality. This violation means that Option (1) is wrong. Options (3), (4), and (5) are not true.

36. **(1)** (Evaluation) More people approved of the president's performance than those who thought the economy would improve. Options (2) and (4) are not supported by the charts. Option (3) may be generally true but is not reflected in the graphs. There is no evidence for Option (5) by the information on the graphs.

37. **(2)** (Application) The people who didn't know probably didn't care one way or the other. Being uninterested does not imply any of the other options.

38. **(3)** (Comprehension) The women organized in order to improve the position of women in society. There is no evidence for the other options in the passage.

39. **(5)** (Application) Gun control is not primarily a women's issue, but it is one that applies equally to all people. The other options are subjects which are of special interest to women.

40. **(3)** (Analysis) The filibusters' actions were politically a waste of time and effort. Legislators filibuster to delay or prevent decisions. Options (1) and (5) are wrong because long-windedness can bore and confuse an audience. Options (2) and (4) have no support in the passage.

41. **(5)** (Comprehension) Spending more money has not improved education. Options (1), (2), and (4) are wrong. There is no evidence for Option (3).

42. **(2)** (Analysis) The effort involved would benefit the students and, therefore, improve test scores. There is no mention of Option (1) or Option (3). Option (4) is not suggested by the passage. Option (5) is what Cavazos wants to avoid.

43. **(3)** (Evaluation) The educational performance of schoolchildren is merely average. The problem does not suggest Option (1) is true. There is no discussion in the passage of Option (2). Option (4) may often be true, but it is not true in all cases. There is no support for Option (5) in the passage.

44. **(4)** (Analysis) Cavazos is concerned with Americans being competitive with Japan and West Germany. Options (1), (3), and (5) do not demonstrate average performance. Option (2) plays a part in the comparison, but figures are not given in the passage.

45. **(1)** (Analysis) Joining a union would have meant accepting that union's political position. Options (2) and (3) imply a faulty cause and effect. Option (4) has no support in the passage. Option (5) is wrong because having fewer members would not end the unions; it would only weaken them.

46. **(4)** (Application) Offering a low property tax rate would be an incentive to a business. Option (3) would drive a business away. Options (1), (2), and (5) are incorrect because a city cannot change state or federal tax rates.

Chapter 5: Behavioral Science (Pages 47–54)

1. **(2)** (Comprehension) The author calls a young child's drawings fanciful and inventive. Options (1), (3), and (4) are contradicted in the passage. Option (5) is wrong because it is not the intention of a young child.

2. **(3)** (Application) Although designed for a child, the coloring book would be the least creative activity. The other options are based on a looseness of expression or technique. In Option (4), realistic depiction is altered by the grain of the material itself.

3. **(1)** (Evaluation) As children mature, their art becomes more conventionally realistic and less dependent on impression. Option (5) is not true. There is no support for Options (2), (3), or (4) in the passage.

4. **(2)** (Analysis) Folk art is strong and simple like a preschooler's work. There is no evidence for Options (1) and (3) in the passage. Options (4) and (5) may be true, but they are not primary reasons for its popularity.

5. **(5)** (Evaluation) Educators have seen tests as the measure of intelligence, and componential intelligence produces good test-taking skills. Options (1), (2), and (4) are wrong because all go beyond the norms with which most educators are comfortable; they are also difficult to measure. Option (3) is expected instead of valued.

6. **(1)** (Application) The most creative of the options is the artist. The other options may involve experiential intelligence but do not rely on it.

7. **(2)** (Evaluation) The practical, adaptive nature of contextual intelligence supports this conclusion. Option (1) might be true in some cases but not in others. Options (3), (4), and (5) are not supported in the passage.

8. **(3)** (Analysis) The tests measure only one of the two types of intelligence. Option (1) has no support. Options (2) and (5) are true but are not explained by the passage. Option (4) is a popular belief not supported in the passage.

9. **(1)** (Application) Scientists assumed that character was a genetic factor that could be passed through heredity. Option (3) is not true. Options (2) and (4) are not probable influences. Option (5) would be believed only by an odd few.

10. **(3)** (Analysis) People often cannot see themselves as others do. Option (1) is wrong because there is conflict between self-perception and reality. There is no support for Options (2) and (5) in the cartoon. Option (4) is wrong because the character is misjudging other people's perceptions.

11. **(1)** (Analysis) Without this assumption the question would not make sense. It also suggests the idea of a pattern of socially acceptable behavior. There is no evidence in the cartoon for Options (2) and (4). Options (3) and (5) are psychologically unsound.

12. **(4)** (Analysis) People continue to accept as true a belief that worked even after it is disproven. There is no evidence in the passage for Options (1) and (3). Options (2) and (5) are too specific to be explained by a description of basic methodology.

13. **(3)** (Application) This statement is too general to be tested and can only serve as a model for specific hypotheses. Options (1) and (2) are, therefore, wrong. There is no evidence for Options (4) and (5) in the passage.

14. **(2)** (Application) This possibility can be researched through interview and observation. Option (1) is a belief and not a testable hypothesis. Options (3) and (4) are wrong because they are facts. Option (5) is based on a social attitude but is not an hypothesis that shows a relation between age role and social expectation.

15. **(3)** (Analysis) Because of the complexity of human behavior, many factors would have to be considered to determine which might be affecting a particular behavior. Option (1) is wrong because sociology is based on the idea that types of behavior are predictable. Option (2) is not true. Option (4) is wrong because many research techniques are used. Option (5) has no bearing on the question.

16. **(2)** (Comprehension) Because some lawyers successfully represent people whom the public views as criminals, lawyers are often considered untrustworthy by the public. Options (1), (3), (4), and (5) are not supported by the cartoon.

17. **(2)** (Application) Criminals and the lawyers who successfully represent them are untrustworthy. Options (1) and (3) contradict the image of the lawyer presented. Options (4) and (5) apply more to the women than to their opinions.

18. **(4)** (Comprehension) Each behavior listed is directly across from its opposite. While Options (3) and (5) may be true, there is no evidence on the diagram. There is no support for Options (1) and (2) in the diagram.

19. **(2)** (Comprehension) Manager X is showing respect by getting up to greet manager O. This most likely means manager X has a lower job status. This eliminates the other options.

20. **(3)** (Evaluation) Attitudes are being communicated without words, so Option (2) is wrong. There is no evidence for Options (1), (4), and (5) on the diagrams.

21. **(4)** (Application) Managers O and X in (D) are in friendly, equal positions. To stand at a distance would indicate a cooling of that interaction, thus eliminating Option (3). Options (1) and (2) are wrong because the movements would not likely create a sudden change in attitude. There is no evidence on the diagram to support Option (5).

22. **(1)** (Analysis) As attitude can be detected by distance patterns alone, distance has social importance. While Options (3) and (4) may be true, they are not supported by these diagrams. There is no evidence for Options (2) and (5) on the diagrams.

23. **(2)** (Evaluation) The Truk adults believe children are not responsible for knowing proper behavior while American adults believe children should learn. There is no support for Options (1), (3), (4), and (5) according to the information given.

24. **(1)** (Application) The image of a simple people is contradicted by the evidence of abstract thought. The passage does not mention Options (2), (3), and (4). Option (5) is not contradicted in the passage.

25. **(2)** (Application) The only example of abstract thought is the writing and mathematical system. Options (1), (3), (4), and (5) involve crafts, subsistence technique, and social structure.

26. **(4)** (Analysis) The language is adapted to express cultural beliefs, not the other way around as suggested in Options (1) and (5).

Option (2) has nothing to do with language. Option (3) is also a result of complexity.

27. **(1)** (Evaluation) The mention of the dead was avoided because of respect, not unpleasantness as suggested in Options (3) and (4). There is no evidence in the passage for Option (2). Option (5) is wrong because the taboo reflects the power of language.

28. **(3)** (Comprehension) Simple addition shows that the family spent more than it received. There is no evidence that Option (2) is true. The figures do not support Options (1), (4), or (5).

29. **(5)** (Evaluation) The amount of bahts spent on food and entertainment reveals the importance of hospitality. There is no information on the chart regarding the other options.

30. **(4)** (Application) Americans do not pay a bride price. All the other options refer to practices both cultures have.

31. **(3)** (Comprehension) Disagreement is indicated by the three different definitions of the peasants. There is no evidence in the passage for the other options.

32. **(2)** (Evaluation) All three definitions refer to some aspect of how a group makes its living. Option (1) is suggested by reference to the elite, but further details would be needed. There is no mention in the passage of Options (3), (4), or (5).

33. **(3)** (Analysis) The new model includes cities and acculturation, aspects not suggested by most studies of non-Western primitive peoples, and it would try to account for the development of the more complex social structures. Options (1) and (2) are not supported in the passage. Option (4) is not true. Option (5) is not supported by the passage and is highly unlikely.

34. **(2)** (Analysis) Conclusions about the overall patterns can be drawn from studies of the details, so those details are important. Option (1) does not address the question. Option (3) is not true. Option (4) cannot be proven. Option (5) is wrong because age has nothing to do with value.

SOCIAL STUDIES TEST

TEST A: SOCIAL STUDIES

1 ①②③④⑤	12 ①②③④⑤	23 ①②③④⑤	34 ①②③④⑤	45 ①②③④⑤	56 ①②③④⑤
2 ①②③④⑤	13 ①②③④⑤	24 ①②③④⑤	35 ①②③④⑤	46 ①②③④⑤	57 ①②③④⑤
3 ①②③④⑤	14 ①②③④⑤	25 ①②③④⑤	36 ①②③④⑤	47 ①②③④⑤	58 ①②③④⑤
4 ①②③④⑤	15 ①②③④⑤	26 ①②③④⑤	37 ①②③④⑤	48 ①②③④⑤	59 ①②③④⑤
5 ①②③④⑤	16 ①②③④⑤	27 ①②③④⑤	38 ①②③④⑤	49 ①②③④⑤	60 ①②③④⑤
6 ①②③④⑤	17 ①②③④⑤	28 ①②③④⑤	39 ①②③④⑤	50 ①②③④⑤	61 ①②③④⑤
7 ①②③④⑤	18 ①②③④⑤	29 ①②③④⑤	40 ①②③④⑤	51 ①②③④⑤	62 ①②③④⑤
8 ①②③④⑤	19 ①②③④⑤	30 ①②③④⑤	41 ①②③④⑤	52 ①②③④⑤	63 ①②③④⑤
9 ①②③④⑤	20 ①②③④⑤	31 ①②③④⑤	42 ①②③④⑤	53 ①②③④⑤	64 ①②③④⑤
10 ①②③④⑤	21 ①②③④⑤	32 ①②③④⑤	43 ①②③④⑤	54 ①②③④⑤	
11 ①②③④⑤	22 ①②③④⑤	33 ①②③④⑤	44 ①②③④⑤	55 ①②③④⑤	

TEST B: SOCIAL STUDIES

1 ①②③④⑤	12 ①②③④⑤	23 ①②③④⑤	34 ①②③④⑤	45 ①②③④⑤	56 ①②③④⑤
2 ①②③④⑤	13 ①②③④⑤	24 ①②③④⑤	35 ①②③④⑤	46 ①②③④⑤	57 ①②③④⑤
3 ①②③④⑤	14 ①②③④⑤	25 ①②③④⑤	36 ①②③④⑤	47 ①②③④⑤	58 ①②③④⑤
4 ①②③④⑤	15 ①②③④⑤	26 ①②③④⑤	37 ①②③④⑤	48 ①②③④⑤	59 ①②③④⑤
5 ①②③④⑤	16 ①②③④⑤	27 ①②③④⑤	38 ①②③④⑤	49 ①②③④⑤	60 ①②③④⑤
6 ①②③④⑤	17 ①②③④⑤	28 ①②③④⑤	39 ①②③④⑤	50 ①②③④⑤	61 ①②③④⑤
7 ①②③④⑤	18 ①②③④⑤	29 ①②③④⑤	40 ①②③④⑤	51 ①②③④⑤	62 ①②③④⑤
8 ①②③④⑤	19 ①②③④⑤	30 ①②③④⑤	41 ①②③④⑤	52 ①②③④⑤	63 ①②③④⑤
9 ①②③④⑤	20 ①②③④⑤	31 ①②③④⑤	42 ①②③④⑤	53 ①②③④⑤	64 ①②③④⑤
10 ①②③④⑤	21 ①②③④⑤	32 ①②③④⑤	43 ①②③④⑤	54 ①②③④⑤	
11 ①②③④⑤	22 ①②③④⑤	33 ①②③④⑤	44 ①②③④⑤	55 ①②③④⑤	